WARWICK TODD
Back in
THE BAGGY GREEN

By the same author

Through to the Keeper
Wieldin' the Willow
Creased Lightning
So, You've Lost Your Licence...
On the Front Foot
Have Bat, Will Travel
The Warwick Todd Liver Cleansing Diet

WARWICK TODD
Back in
THE BAGGY GREEN

THE AUSTRALIAN CRICKET LEGEND WRITES AGAIN!

AS TOLD TO TOM GLEISNER

ABC
BOOKS

Published by ABC Books for the
AUSTRALIAN BROADCASTING CORPORATION
GPO Box 9994 Sydney NSW 2001

Copyright © Tom Gleisner 1998

First published November 1998

National Library of Australia
Cataloguing-in-Publication entry
Gleisner, Tom, 1962- .
Back in the baggy green

ISBN 0 7333 0688 8.

1. Cricket — Humor.
I. Australian Broadcasting Corporation.
II. Title.

796.3580207

Designed and typeset by
Deborah Brash/Brash Design Pty Ltd
in 11/17pt Stone Informal
Cover designed by Robert Taylor
Photo manipulations by Robert Taylor
Printed and bound in Australia by
Australian Print Group, Maryborough, Victoria

2 4 5 3 1

Acknowledgments

Production Assistance: Susannah Mott and Debra Choate
Warwick's commemorative plate and print: Carrie Kennedy
Photography: David Lott
Additional photography: David Mitchiner
And one or two other shots: Joanne Donahoe and Debra Choate

Special thanks to:
Ben Morieson, Annabel Wang, Steven Clode, Joanne Donahoe, the Very Reverend Fr Michael Hirsh, Polly Watkins, Nikki Hamilton, Billy Pinnell, Glenn Robbins, Vanitha Naidu, Radha Naidu, Jo Woods, Michelle Burch, Matthew Rooke, Jason Mee, Kathy Lane, Mr Bert Newton.

Thanks also to:
The Melbourne Cricket Club; the MCG scoreboard; the Greyhound Hotel, St Kilda; Lonergan Funerals; Melbourne High School; Rebel Sport; Fosters Asia; Roshan's Fashions and to Santo, Jane, Rob and Michael — my Working Dog partners.

Dedication

I dedicate this book to the
person who has stood by me through
thick and thin, providing
encouragement, support, confidence
and, above all, love.

Also, to my wife Ros.

Foreword

by Deano

If everyone in the Australian team is a top bloke, which of course they are, then Warwick Todd must rate as one of the most top. A natural-born larrikin, a man who likes a punt and a beer as much as he loves scoring runs (especially against the Poms!), Toddy is the quintessential Australian cricketer: tough, aggressive, always ready for a fight. And he displays much the same qualities on the field.

I'm reminded of what Allan Border once said: 'He is a man for all seasons, someone you can depend upon in all situations.' Even though AB was talking about Boonie, I feel those words could equally apply to Toddy.

Like me he's had a few run-ins with authority, ruffled a few feathers, put the odd nose out of joint. But the occasional assualt charge will never stop this big-hearted Aussie, a man with green and gold pumping through his veins. And you know what? Beneath that tough exterior there lurks a big-hearted softie. I remember heading to South Africa together in '94. The in-flight movie was *Bridges of Madison County* and looking across to where Toddy was sitting I swear I detected a tear in the big man's eye. Turned out a cabin attendant had just informed him the bar was closed.

The world of international cricket can be a tough one. It's fiercely competitive and there were times when Toddy and I were fighting for the same position on the team. Out on the field tensions ran high and abuse would often fly. But back in the rooms, over a few cold beers, it was a different story. The abuse would still fly but a lot less coherently.

Toddy has notched up just about more Tests, runs and match fines than any other player around. He's been there through the good times — the '87 World Cup, England in '89 and '93 — and through the bad — his fourth book, *Collected Poems*, sold only 200 copies. But hopefully this latest publication will put him back on the best-seller lists. It describes in painstaking detail the Aussie's 1998 tour of India, a tour in which Toddy took the Indian attack by the scruff of the turban and gave it fair buggery.

Good on ya, Toddy!

Deano

Introduction

A few years ago I was flicking through my old notebooks in search of tour memorabilia for an upcoming auction when I came across this entry, written in England during the Ashes tour of '93:

Slept in. Down to breakfast then training session. Went out for a drink after dinner. The next day Boonie slept in and almost missed the bus.

Reading that simple, elegant prose as it unfolded over the next forty or fifty pages a thought struck me. What a fabulously interesting book it would make. And so the career of Warwick Todd, writer, was born. Since that time I've had the privilege of writing seventeen cricket books. Not a lot by today's standards I know, but I like to feel I've made a small contribution to this vital genre. And when I was re-called to play in the '98 tour to India I decided to add one more to that list (two, if you count *Toddy's Tuscan Cookbook*, which is still at the printer's). *Back in the Baggy Green* tells the story of my recall to the Australian team and the tour to India that followed. Every day is covered in fascinating detail pieced together from personal notes, player interviews and police records, making up an unique insight into life on tour. The heat, the hardship, the highs and the lows, it's all part of *Back in the Baggy Green*. (Except for Chapter Seven, which had to be omitted following threats from Tony Greig's lawyer.)

Preface

There was a time when Australian cricketers dreaded a tour of India. It was viewed as a two-month prison sentence during which team members would have to endure substandard accommodation, indifferent food and parochial fans, all in a depressing, bleak atmosphere. It was very much like playing Shield cricket in Perth. But I didn't care about the hardships, I was just glad to be back in the baggy green...

On a Personal Note...

As a high-profile, successful and popular Australian sportsman it's virtually impossible for someone like me to have a private life. Even though I yearn to be treated as just a normal bloke, it seems that everyone wants a piece of Warwick Todd™ and I know that most aspects of my personal life will inevitably end up under the media spotlight. And to some extent I can't really complain about this — after all, I do employ a full-time publicist to make sure it keeps happening. But there is a line, a point at which media interest can become media intrusion. It's one thing to have dozens of cameras trained on you out in the middle of the SCG, but not when you're simply going about your daily business, shopping, relaxing or emerging from the Family Court.

Which brings me to Ros. As the entire world seems to know, my wife and I have been through a rough patch. I make no bones about the fact. But it was always something we were going to work out between us. If the press had just backed off and given us a little space then that — along with the anger-management classes and interim restraining order — would have been all we needed. But no, they had to keep intruding, poking their noses in. One morning last year I woke to find a bloke with a telephoto lens outside my window taking photos of me. I ran outside and threatened to report him to the Press Council only to find out he wasn't a reporter but a private detective hired by Ros. But that's just an example of the pressure-cooker world we celebrities inhabit.

Anyway, Ros and I sorted out our differences and I'm pleased to say that our marriage is now as strong as it has ever been. The demands of modern cricket are such that balancing work and family life is never going to be easy but I feel I've made a pretty good fist of it. To this end I'm eternally grateful to my wife Roslyn and two daughters Raleisha and the younger one whose name temporarily escapes me.

One Strange Summer

As the first cicadas of summer began their shrill chorus and I peeled the cover off our pool to reveal the stagnant body of mosquito-infested water beneath, I realised two things. Firstly, Apollo Pumps would have to be the worst manufacturers of in-ground pool filter systems in Australia. The so-called 'space-age' fibreglass finish rusted within a week, one leaf only has to float past the skimmer box and it immediately jams, and as for the pump, it's so loud we've already had three separate complaints from the neighbours. Not that they're exactly silent themselves, jabbering away in Hong Kong-ese half the bloody night. The only positive is I got the entire pool package for free, thanks to a small endorsement.

'Hit Summer for Six!'

'In my opinion Apollo is Australia's number one manufacturer of pool and pump systems. Their space-age filter system takes the worry out of pool-cleaning, which means I can 'score' more 'runs' by relaxing at home...'

The other thing I realised was that for the first time in almost a decade, I would not be playing cricket for my country.

After I returned from England in late 1997 I was keen to have a break from cricket. I calculated that during my career I'd been away on tour for something like eight years out of twelve. That's a lot of time away from your loved ones and Ros, and I decided to spend some quality time together — just us and the kids enjoying ourselves as a family. And it was a great afternoon but I soon found myself with 'itchy feet' again. On top of that, I still needed to keep the money rolling in. Not that I'd exactly been letting the grass grow under my feet. Since my shock axing from the Australian team last year, W Todd™ has been kept pretty busy with corporate and promotional work. It's amazing the demand for sporting stars, whether it's revving sales staff up at motivational seminars or giving after-dinner speeches. The money is good too, and I basically found I could give the same talk wherever I went. Obviously you tone down some of the 'bluer' material

THE CLUB YARRAWONGA
New Year's Eve Dinner Dance
FEATURING ALL-STAR AFTER-DINNER ENTERTAINMENT!
• Ron Blaskett and Gerry G!
• Elvis Prezley (Cobram's number one Elvis Presley impersonator)!
• And special guest, former Australian Test hero Warwick Todd!
• Tickets available at the door

Oz Inspirational Ltd present...
3RD ANNUAL SMALL BUSINESS SEMINAR
Featuring top local and international motivational speakers
DAVID MCKILLOP (CEO Montage Pty Ltd)
DR SAUL TOERVST (Business Psychologist)
WARWICK TODD (Australian sportsman and former bankrupt)

if you're talking to kids and I discovered that Baptists don't take too kindly to the old 'in-out' word, but apart from that it's easy money, cash in the hand, and you're out the door.

My other main source of income when not playing cricket is product endorsements. It's amazing the number of people who want either an ex-sportsman or John Laws pretending to use their product. Of course, you have to be a little selective.

'Late nights, poor diet, too much alcohol, no exercise. As an Australian cricketer I know the dangers...' W Todd

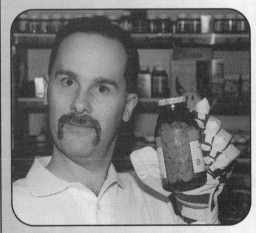

That's why 'Toddy' uses and recommends KARMA low-cost vitamin-style capsules. By cutting down on unnecessary expenses like packaging and testing, KARMA vitamin-style capsules provide the cheapest pick-me-up around. And as Toddy says... 'They give me the energy to make a century every day!'

But there's more to life than money (that's actually a quote from one of my motivational lectures and therefore copyright) and I was keen to pursue other avenues. I've always been interested in becoming involved with the media, preferably radio or TV. Quite a few ex-cricketers have done well on TV and it doesn't seem to require much natural talent or training — just look at Mike Whitney.

The most obvious possibility was joining the Channel 9 commentary team but, as I discovered, this is not as easy as it seems. I believe that technically you have to wait for a current member to die, resign or be suspended after an ugly airport lounge incident. But as it turned out, it was radio that gave me my first big break in the world of media. It was late November and I got a call from Jim Maxwell, who wondered if I'd be interested in joining the ABC commentary team. They were covering a Shield match in Tassie and needed someone to help with the stats. Even though the on-air component would be minimal I felt it was an exciting opportunity to show what I had to offer.

Unfortunately I was never asked back to the ABC commentary team but as they say in the classics, 'when one door closes another opens'.

R E H A M E
MEDIA MONITORING

HOBART 7ZR
25 NOVEMBER 1997
BROADCAST OF TASMANIA VS QUEENSLAND SHEFFIELD SHIELD MATCH

MAXWELL: And that's called wide by Umpire Randell, Kasprowicz obviously having a little trouble with his rhythm. How many wides is that now Warwick?

TODD: Eh?

MAXWELL: How many wides has Kasprowicz bowled?

TODD: Dunno. (PAUSE) Have to be a shitload.

(That's also a quote from one of my motivational lectures.) It was shortly before Christmas when my manager Gabe lined me up a TV gig. It wasn't cricket related, in fact it was a documentary series for cable TV called *Warwick Todd's World of Nature*. All I had to do was sit at a desk and say 'And now here's a doco about zebras' and pretend to look interested. Money wasn't great but you could knock off forty episodes in an afternoon.

But for all the work that was coming my way there was still something missing in my life, and that something was cricket. No sooner had I returned from the Ashes tour of England last year than I was wishing I could be off

Unfortunately I was never asked back to the ABC commentary team.

'And now, here's a doco about zebras...'

on another trip. Funnily enough, Ros felt the same way. Hanging round the house all summer watching the boys play New Zealand and South Africa — I wanted to be out there. The closest I could get was leading a supporter's tour to New Zealand in January for the four one-day internationals. When each of those games was marred by unprecedented levels of crowd misbehaviour, I knew I still had something to offer Australian cricket.

Since my shock axing from the Australian squad in '97 I'd kept in touch with the selectors. I followed Trevor Hohns' car home for a few nights and just sat outside his house, watching. There's little doubt in my mind that the powers-that-be wanted me out of the side, regardless of form. I was seen as a 'troublemaker', a loose cannon who couldn't be trusted to uphold the team image. But the gods must have been smiling on me because late last summer the Australian team was struck down by a run of injuries. Bowlers like Pigeon, Gilly, Lee and Bic all broke down. Meanwhile a few batsmen like Herb, BJ and Lang were struggling to make runs. Result: a late night phone call to the home of W Todd asking if he'd be prepared to pull on the pads for a tour of India. Now let me be honest, I didn't immediately say yes. Instead, I got out a pen and paper and wrote down all the negatives and all the positives of heading away on another trip.

Negatives	Positives
India a tough tour	Mateship
Constant travel	Good money
Serious training	Possible new book deal
Steve Waugh	Chance to boost average
Away from kids for 2 months	Away from kids for 2 months

I said yes.

Day 1 ✌ (Fri Feb 20)

Sydney to Hong Kong

Packing bags for a long overseas trip is never easy, especially the amount of gear we cricketers take away with us. Over the years I've developed a routine that makes sure everything is remembered: clothes, toiletries, equipment and, last of all, the baggy green cap. Nothing could be more precious to a player than his Australian cap, presented on the eve of your first Test match. Steve 'Tugga' Waugh still has his original, as do most of the boys; you're only ever entitled to a new one in pretty special circumstances, such as if it's stolen or tossed off a moving bus or set on fire. I treasure every one of the twenty-seven I've owned.

Outside I could hear the taxi tooting. Time to go. Final moments at home prior to leaving on a long tour are always precious, the chance to spend a few special moments with loved ones before the inevitable sad goodbyes. So it was unfortunate Ros was out having her fringe trimmed when the time came for me to leave but she did leave a farewell post-it note on the fridge.

It was midmorning as I reached Sydney airport and made my way towards the international departure lounge. As usual there was a mass of people inside and I wondered how I would find my team-mates. Fortunately Heals was easy to spot, as he was standing on the bar leading a pre-tour squad singalong.

Sydney airport, fortunately Heals was easy to spot.

1

It was great to catch up with the guys again and there was a mood of excitement in the air. A couple of the lads arrived with rather bad haircuts and were immediately singled out for humiliation by the rest of us. There's nothing quite like someone else's misfortune to bring us all closer together.

The twenty-man squad heading for India included our long-time physio Hooter, scorer Mike Walsh and team manager Steve 'Brute' Bernard whose job it is to say no to as many official functions as possible. Our first official function of the tour was a few farewell drinks for our tour sponsor, Foster's, which was quite enjoyable until our tour sponsors insisted on joining us. I tell you what, standing round making idle chitchat with company executives is one of the real downers of modern-day cricket. But without the sponsorship dollars I guess we wouldn't get very far so it's important to maintain good public relations, even with boring bastards like the people from Foster's.

Every time the Aussie squad travels I'm amazed by the amount of gear we take with us and this tour was no exception. In all we're carrying seventy-six items, including suitcases, coffins, medical supplies and Adam Dale.

As usual the press was out in force, desperately seeking shots of loving couples saying goodbye. Not that the Waugh twins would oblige. The press was also seeking interviews and quotes from all of us players. I used to get a little flustered in situations like this but that was before the ACB had the foresight to run player training sessions in the art of handling the media. Let's face it, most journos are always on the lookout for a provocative or sensational headline but I'm pleased to say these days W Todd knows better than to provide one.

Once customs had been cleared it was time for a bit of shopping, with adaptor plugs, blow-up cushions, batteries and tapes all being jettisoned to make room for several bottles of Jim Beam and a carton of smokes.

The flight from Sydney to Honkers passed without incident, apart from a minor food fight that got a little out of hand. It began when

'Second rate team' says Todd

Australian Test batsman Warwick Todd today delivered a stinging attack on his team-mates selected for the upcoming tour of India. In an exclusive interview at Sydney airport before heading off, Todd also hit out at tour selectors, Sir Donald Bradman and the Dalai Lama before

Slats up-ended his tray of dessert over the poor player seated in front, one P Wilson. Blocker naturally enough decided to take out revenge by tipping the contents of his meal over the player in front of him. This chain of good-natured food-fighting eventually reached yours truly, who joined in by emptying the contents of his wine bottle over the next victim in line. Who happened to be the pilot. Apparently a couple of fuses in the flight console blew and there was a bit of trouble getting the navigational software re-booted, but apart from that there were no real problems.

We touched down in Hong Kong late afternoon. As this was only an overnight stay we checked into the Regal Airport Hotel where a few of the younger guys headed for the gym. Personally, I think this obsession with fitness is a worrying trend creeping into the game with blokes like Slats and Blewie too busy lifting weights to experience the sights and sounds of a foreign land. So I was pleased to join Heals, Pistol and Junior on a trip downtown to sample the local culture. Quite a few bottles of it, from memory.

Day 2 ✌ (Sat Feb 21)

Hong Kong to Bombay

Woke this morning feeling hot and stuffy. As I tried desperately to open the hotel room window to get a little air I was set upon by a couple of air hostesses. Turned out we were 33 000 feet above sea level, en route to Bombay. How I got on the flight remains a complete blur. (Apparently team manager Steve 'Brute' Bernard carried me on as hand luggage.)

The rest of the flight passed without incident and we soon heard those familiar words, 'Ladies and gentlemen, as we're about to land in Bombay would you kindly return to your seats and untie the Chief Purser.'

We touched down in Bombay and made our way through a throng of customs officials, security guards and journos, all asking the same old questions: 'Are you looking forward to the tour?' 'How do you think the team will go?' 'Did you realise the limit for duty-free liquor is not seven litres?'

Outside the airport there was an even larger crowd waiting to greet us. There's nothing that can really prepare you for the shock of India — the sights, the smells, the overwhelming crush of humanity. Within seconds of leaving the airport the entire team was surrounded by autograph hunters and well-wishers. It's amazing how one comment can put everything in perspective. Stepping towards the bus a young child approached me with an autograph book and said, 'Welcome, Mr Todd. Well played in '96.' You realise just how much this game means to people. This kid, who remembered me from the World Cup, had obviously waited in scorching heat for hours, just to get an autograph. In hindsight perhaps I should have given him one.

While one fan tries to shake the hand of our star leg-spinner the short bloke behind was pinching his wallet. Welcome to India.

We checked into the Taj Mahal Hotel in downtown Bombay where a team meeting was scheduled for 6.00. The main subject addressed was health, always a worry when touring the subcontinent. Back in '69 when Bill Lawry's team toured India, team management was forbidden from taking special foods, believing that to do so would be an insult to their hosts. How times have changed! Now of course it's expected that visiting Australian cricketers will insult their hosts. Accordingly, our manager has brought across a dozen jars of Vegemite, a carton of Mars Bars and numerous other goodies unavailable here. As a further safety measure, all our meals at grounds will be prepared by chefs at the Taj hotels where we are staying. On the possible chance that some-one does find themselves eating in an unknown restaurant Hooter had some good advice: 'Look at the meal, touch it to ensure it is piping hot, smell it and closely examine it. Then reject it and head for McDonald's.' Of course, not all players are so worried by the possibility of food poisoning. Some guys I've toured with take the attitude 'she'll be right' and basically end up eating anything they like. This approach, known as 'doing a Merv', can work for some but I'll try to be a little more cautious.

As for water, we have been issued strict instructions to only ever drink the bottled variety, or stick to beer. To be extra safe I think I'll do both — and only drink bottled beer.

Day 3 ✌ (Sun Feb 22)

Coming down to breakfast this morning there must have been 200 locals in the hotel lobby, milling about desperately seeking autographs and photos with any player foolish enough to walk past. I asked the concierge why there weren't any security guards posted at the front door to keep these people out and he replied, 'They are the security guards.'

Outside the hotel there were even more fans, waving and smiling as we made our way to the team bus. The crowd was so dense that soldiers with canes had to beat a path through the swarming mass just to allow us to reach the bus. I saw men, women and even children receive terrible blows as we completed the short journey. Imagine how bad I felt when I realised I'd left my wallet back at the hotel and another baton charge had to be organised just for me to go and collect it.

Imagine how bad I felt when I realised I'd left my wallet back at the hotel...

Our practice session today was at Bombay's famous Gymkhana Club. After several days of travel you might expect the Aussie squad to have had a day off but fitness and match toughness are a major part of this tour. So much so that we've agreed to power walk during every pub crawl.

Today's workout was planned by the ever-sadistic Hooter and involved five 'stations':

1) A five-minute jog (warm-up).
2) Three minutes of shoulder work.
3) Three minutes of stomach work (crunches, leg lifts).
4) Ten minutes of brisk cycling.
5) A five-minute jog (warm-down).

I tell you, by the end of the session I was absolutely knackered and dreading tomorrow when we're expected to tackle stations 2 to 5.

Fortunately, however, lunch was excellent and was followed by a nap, after which we enjoyed a good net session, with all of us adjusting for the slower Indian wickets. Then we made our way back to the hotel in time for tonight's official function — a cocktail party put on by hotel management.

Day 4 ✌ (Mon Feb 23)

With our first tour match just a day away it was decided this morning to up the intensity, hence a hideous 10.00 am wake-up call. As is standard policy on Australian tours, senior players like myself are all rooming with younger blokes and I've got the South Australian batsman Darren Lehmann. Boof seems a nice bloke though of course he's a little overawed about being on his first tour. I gave him the same advice I give all new-comers to the Australian team: relax, be yourself, enjoy your cricket, feel part of the squad and never look Tubs directly in the eye. Talking to the younger blokes and making them feel part of the team is an important function for us senior players. I well remember my first international tour. I was rooming with the great Dennis Lillee. The night before our first match I lay in bed so excited all I could do was talk about myself — my hopes, my plans for the future, what I wanted to achieve from cricket. Fot was such a good listener he barely uttered a word. You could have easily mistaken him for being asleep.

Despite the early hour the heat and humidity were already high, as was the pollution level. A thick grey smog hung in the air and the toxic fumes were so bad that team management took the drastic measure of banning smoking on the bus.

Today's session at the Gymkhana Club was devoted to fielding, with Tubs and Swampy hitting a succession of high balls and then yelling a player's name. This drill called for pretty good reflexes because once you heard your name you didn't have much time to get out of your deckchair, jump the beer garden fence and reach the ball before it landed.

During lunch the team for tomorrow's match against Mumbai was named, with the Waugh brothers and McGill sitting out. As this was our first match of the tour Tubs took the opportunity to speak about

Fielding skills and fitness go hand in hand at training.

the weeks ahead, encouraging us all to set individual goals. Personally I'd like to score a lot of runs and perhaps stitch up a few new sponsorship deals here on the subcontinent. It would also be good if the team did well.

This afternoon saw me visiting our team physio for some work on my troublesome knee. It's flared up a little in the past few days but Hooter says there's nothing to worry about provided I avoid aggravating it by not doing anything silly. So I'll be avoiding as much training as possible.

A quiet night, as is customary before any tour match, saw the boys relaxing with a few nightcaps at the Taj Hotel bar. Tomorrow the battle begins…!

Day 5 ✌ (Tues Feb 24)

Mumbai vs Australia, Day 1

Woke this morning feeling pretty good, apart from a stiff neck courtesy of falling asleep at the Taj Hotel bar. After a quick shower and break-fast it was off to the Brabourne Stadium where Tubs did the right thing and won the toss. As I was not required on-field immediately I agreed to do an interview with Star TV, India's leading pay-TV network, which is covering the tour. Asked about the huge crowd that had turned out for this match I quipped, 'The spectators are packed so close together it's little wonder most of you Indians turn out to be poofs!' Naturally I was joking and even gave a little wink to emphasise the fact but unfor-tunately the interview was terminated at that point as the bloke I was talking to had some sort of coughing fit. Anyway, I made it back to our rooms just in time to see Slats and Tubby walk to the crease. It's great to see Slats back in the Aussie line-up. Of course, it was here in India that his Test career 'ended' after he made a wide, wild slash at a ball in Delhi and was out for a duck. It's funny how one misjudged stroke can cost you a career. A similar thing once happened to me at the 'Gabba in '95 when I swung wildly at the chairman of selectors Trevor Hohns' rear tail-light in the car park. Anyway, many felt Slats was far too impetuous and rash for Test cricket but there's no doubt the young New South Welshman has tamed this 'exuberant' side of his game, as was evident from the first ball he faced this morning. Kuruvilla pitched one up, Slats aimed a big drive, got an inside edge and squirted the ball to square leg. I've never seen him so restrained.

Unfortunately Tubs was also quite restrained, getting out for 5 after chopping a ball onto his pads and then his stumps. But Blewie, Ponts, Heals and yours truly all got starts, taking us to 8-305 at stumps. Slats

Warney has an enormous amount under his belt.

fell just two runs short of his century, ending a great return to international cricket.

Chatting over a few drinks after play we all agreed the slow pitch was offering plenty of assistance to the spinners. It'll be great to see Warney and Robbo in action tomorrow. Robbo is a newcomer to the team, with very few first class games under his belt, while of course Warney has an enormous amount under his belt.

You can have a lot of fun in Honkers, even on the cheap. This rickshaw cost just seven bucks an hour. As did the chick.

Taking time out of
our busy schedule
to buy a few duty
free gifts.

Warney arrives on the team bus.

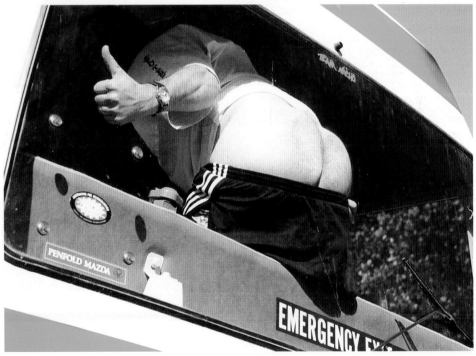

Toddy departs on the team bus.

In Delhi I was thrilled to play in a charity match against HRH Prince Charles.

And even more excited when he fell victim to a Todd bouncer!

Day 6 ✌ (Wed Feb 25)

Mumbai vs Australia, Day 2

Tubs declared this morning at our overnight score and we set about trying to dismiss the home team, a task that proved more difficult than we had hoped. By lunch things were looking really bad; not only were they 3 for 135 with dangerman Tendulkar on 35 not out, the chicken murgh makhani was seriously overcooked. If bloody Indians can't get a curry right, what are they good for? Batting, as it turned out. The afternoon session saw the home team cut loose, dispatching our bowlers to all points of the ground. Tubs tried just about everyone, including Lehmann, but that man Tendulkar raced towards a double century. Now I'm not wanting to criticise Tubs (I'll leave that to anyone who knows anything about cricket), but I felt he could have given me a bowl. I may not have much pace but there's a fair bit in the old Todd arm-ball, especially when I land it on the wicket. Still, it's not for a player to push himself forward in this sort of situation; all you can do is hope to attract your skipper's attention with subtle little warm-up exercises.

Despite only being a 'tour match' there was a fair bit of tension out on the field and a few words were exchanged. Verbally abusing an opposition batsman, or 'sledging' as it is often known, can be a very effective tool. Naturally not everyone approves of it. Back before the 1994 tour of South Africa ACB chairman Dennis Crompton went so far as to state publicly that he wanted to stamp sledging out of the game. He told us abusing people was unmanly and un-Australian. Naturally we told him to get f*#ked. As it turned out, nothing we said to the home team batsmen could stop them racing along to 410 before declaring late in the afternoon, leaving us with a first innings deficit of 105 runs. Tubs managed to whittle that target down to just 104

All you can do is hope to attract your skipper's attention with subtle little warm-up exercises.

before departing the scene, followed by Slats who went for only 4. At this point the obvious move would have been to send in a night-watchman, someone with a steady nerve and rock-solid technique to hold the innings together. But Ponts and I were in the middle of a card game so instead we sent Robbo who lasted just three balls. At stumps we were 3 for 12 and facing an up-hill battle to save the game.

Back at the hotel I rang home to speak with Ros and catch up on family news. Right now we're in the middle of major extensions to the home, adding on a sunroom and new living area. It's something we've planned for quite a while and the builder was due to start this month when suddenly I was selected for this tour. I suggested to Ros that we perhaps postpone construction until I got back as she wouldn't want a whole lot of brickies, plumbers and carpenters on top of her while I was away but she seemed quite determined. Anyway, the good news is Barry (Geeton, of Geeton Constructions) arrived last Monday and has already started the groundwork.

Day 7 ✌ 🐛 (Thur Feb 26)

Mumbai vs Australia, Day 3

Before leaving the hotel this morning Tubs called a special team meeting during which he spoke about the need for a big effort today. He stressed that despite this *only* being a *tour* match it was an important lead-up to the Test series and we had to all give 100 per cent — for our fans, our country and ourselves. It was an inspiring meeting and much appreciated by every one of the five players who showed up. The rest of us received transcripts on the bus.

Unfortunately the Indian spinners got the better of us, dismissing Ponts, Blewie and Boof cheaply. When I came in I knew the situation called for positive play and immediately lofted right-arm tweaker Rajesh Sutar down the ground for four. It's always nice to middle a ball early and I felt confident of building a big innings when the very next ball I fell victim to one of the worst umpiring decisions in the history of cricket. Obviously Mr SK Bhramanan felt the ball was going to hit my wicket (despite pitching three-quarters of a mile outside leg stump) and, as a professional cricketer I had to accept his decision. In the same way he no doubt accepted his bribe money from some Bombay-based gambling syndicate holding big odds on a home team win. After I departed the crease the boys pretty much fell apart to be all out for 135 and Bombay had little trouble knocking off the required runs for a 10 wicket victory.

On a positive note, we didn't let the loss get us down. Naturally things were a little subdued in the dressing room with some of the players even turning to light beer but a good time was still had by all. As usual we senior players all had quite a few media responsibilities, including interviews and photo sessions. The Bombay Press Club was holding a dinner and wanted someone to give a speech, for which I volunteered. With Tubs struggling in the batting department we're all trying to lighten the load on him by sharing a few media responsibilities (and not telling him about our secret meetings). Besides, after-dinner speaking is something I quite enjoy. Over the years you develop a pretty standard talk that you can just trot out whatever the occasion. I usually like to keep the mood light and tend to open with a humorous anecdote involving Merv Hughes in South Africa. The big fella was being hit all over the ground and so at one point he stepped down the pitch, farted, and said to the batsman, 'Try hitting that mate.' This story is a guaranteed ice-breaker and I can only think of one occasion when it's failed to get a laugh: at a function in England. And just between you and me, I don't think the Queen Mother would recognise a joke if it bit her on the arse.

The Queen Mother wouldn't recognise a joke if it bit her on the arse.

Day 8 ✌ (Fri Feb 27)

A hideously early wake-up call this morning saw the room of Messrs Todd and Reiffel looking like a bombsite as we struggled to pack our bags in time for a 7.30 am departure. Just to make matters worse, I received a phone call from yet another crazed Indian cricket fan who somehow got through to our room and obviously wanted a good long chat.

'How are you this morning?'

'Busy mate.'

'What is it that you are doing?'

'Packing.'

'What is your favourite colour?'

Honestly, had I not hung up these sorts of mindless questions could have gone on for hours. It was like being interviewed by Tim Webster. (Only this guy at least knew who I was.)

We eventually made it to the bus and reached the airport where — surprise, surprise — our plane had been delayed. The thought of sitting in some departure lounge surrounded by marauding autograph-hunters was not a pleasant one but fortunately airport security was on hand to prevent anyone bothering us for a signature. They achieved this by bothering us for autographs themselves, until eventually, thankfully, our plane was ready for boarding. Once in the air we were all offered a hot drink (Coke or Fanta) as we cruised towards Vishakhapatnam, a coastal town roughly the size of Brisbane.

Upon arriving at the hotel we were greeted in the traditional Indian manner: a garland of flowers, a red dot between the eyes and no record of our hotel booking. Fortunately tour manager Brute Bernard went into action, demanding the hotel find us all rooms, which they eventually managed to do. I ended up sharing with Heals, who I left handwashing a pair of his glove liners while I headed downstairs to

Another fitness session at the pool.

the pool. Sitting round in airports and cramped planes all day is not exactly ideal for maintaining fitness and can often leave you feeling a little stiff so it was great to really stretch out with a poolside fitness session. I might even have had a swim, had I not fallen asleep on the banana lounge.

At the team meeting it was revealed that our skipper Tubby Taylor had become the first official health victim of the tour (not counting hangovers). Tubs was suffering severe headaches, a possible reaction to his malaria tablets. Personally I've never bothered with these tablets, finding that you can minimise the danger of mosquito bite by keeping windows shut, wearing long sleeves and not showering more than once a fortnight. Anyway, Tubs will be forced to sit out tomorrow's tour match, with Ponts taking his place and Tugga stepping in as skipper. It's a blow for our captain who was keen to play after making just 5 and 1 in the last match but, as I quipped to him on the bus, 'You'll have plenty of other chances to fail!'

After walking back to the hotel and enjoying a few drinks at the hotel bar it was decided to hold an impromptu team barbecue — always a good way of getting the boys together and unwinding after a long day on the road. Naturally a few more cleansing ales were consumed as we stood round cooking the snags and it looked like turning into a top night until the fire sprinklers in Swampy's room went off and we were forced to move outside.

Day 9 ✌ (Sat Feb 28)

President's XI vs Australia, Day 1

As the sun rose over the Indian Ocean this morning I opened the window of Room 407 and took in a deep breath of putrid air wafting up from the open sewer running past our hotel. Not a great way to start the day, but still a vast improvement on the aftershave Heals was liberally applying. Of more concern was the temperature: not yet 8.00 am and already it was well into the thirties. It's on days like this that your twelfth man is kept busy, supplying drinks and sustenance to his hardworking team-mates, and it wasn't long before Boof was being called upon. I asked him to bring some coffee and toast up to my room but he flatly refused, which I think showed a distinct lack of team spirit. No wonder he's only twelfth man.

Down at the ground a steady flow of spectators was filling the concrete terraces. Estimating crowd numbers is always a little difficult in India. It's usually done by a formula that involves working out how many tickets have been sold and then multiplying this figure by thirty. People were packed into every conceivable viewing point, some even balancing on the terrace roofs. About the only unoccupied area was the non-smoking stand.

Tugga failed his first test as stand-in captain, losing the toss and forcing us to field first. As expected, the heat was fierce and conserving energy was an absolute necessity. So when Ramesh got onto an over-pitched Reiffel outswinger and dispatched it towards the boundary, I decided to give up the chase a little earlier than normal. Pretty much as soon as he hit it. To be honest, it was a rubbish ball and deserved to be hit for four anyway. Well, you should have heard Pistol give it to me during the next drinks break. He let fly with a stream of abuse

The non-smoking stand at Vishakhapatnam.

that should have been reserved for the opposition batsmen. He eventually calmed down and I promised to run a little harder the next time he got hit to the fence, which, given his recent bowling, was sure to be pretty soon.

By the end of the day we'd restricted the home side to just 223 runs for the loss of 4 wickets. I can sure tell you the cold beers went down pretty well after play. Replacing lost fluid is a vital part of keeping up match fitness and something I take very seriously. According to the boffins, an average player can lose up to three litres (or one-third of a slab) in a day. After heading back to the hotel a few of the younger boys were in the mood to kick on at a local nightclub but I was feeling just about done in. And, though it hurts to admit it, I'm starting to get a little tired of nightclubs. Loud music, alcohol, smoke — we get enough of that on the team bus.

Day 10 ✌ (Sun Mar 1)

President's XI vs Australia, Day 2

More health worries for the team this morning with Tugga being forced to withdraw because of the dreaded 'Delhi belly' (much to the mirth of all the lads). It's frightening how quickly this condition can strike; when I left our stand-in skipper last night he looked so healthy he was even going back for a second serve of prawn kebabs. But by the time we returned to the hotel he was looking as sick as a dog (much to the mirth of the lads). With both Tubs and Tugga out of action the obvious question arose: 'Who would captain the team today?' As one of the senior members of the side I felt more than capable of doing

the job and must confess to a slight tingle of excitement when I received an urgent message that Tugga wanted to see me in his room. Turned out he wanted more dunny paper. Frankly, I think that's a twelfth man sort of job.

Tugga's room.

Down at the ground play got under way on time, with the home team surviving another good bowling session without loss. As it turned out, Warney was named acting captain and certainly kept us all busy with his imaginative field placings. As a bowler he has an unique ability to work out exactly where a batsman is likely to hit the ball, and then not put a man there. With few wickets falling and the runs flowing freely a few 'pleasantries' were naturally directed towards the batsmen. In any serious sporting contest there's always going to be the odd word said in the heat of battle and provided it's kept in check I have no problem with that. However, we Aussies absolutely draw the line at comments of a racial nature — for us racist sledging is simply not on. The only team to really go in for it is the West Indies but then again, they are black. Despite all our efforts, both physical and verbal, the home team had little trouble reaching 4 for 329 before declaring shortly after lunch. We immediately began the run chase, with Slats and Blewie in devastating form. Blewie fell for 57 but we maintained the momentum, reaching 1 for 269, with Slats unbeaten on 149. You should have seen the young New South Welshman after coming off the ground! He was running round the room, shaking everyone's hand, wanting to phone his wife, talking about a second book. I guess when you consider he's just returned from a sixteen month exile from the game it's pretty understandable. But still a little tedious.

Going into Day Three of the match we're in a good position but of course there's no room for complacency, a point I'm sure Swampy will be making to every one of the boys as soon as they get back from tonight's pub crawl.

Day 11 ✌ (Mon Mar 2)

President's XI vs Australia, Day 3

The good news this morning is that Tubs is feeling a lot better and should even be up to a few net sessions later in the day. The bad news is he's also up to a team meeting, called for 6.30 tonight. Unfortunately Tugga is still crook and unlikely to bat in this game, unless given permission to use both a runner and a portaloo.

Down at the ground Slats and Ponts quickly re-opened their accounts, pushing the run rate along until Slats, on 207, fell victim to the sort of miserable umpiring you only ever get in India. Or Pakistan. (And quite often in New Zealand come to think of it.) He attempted to swing off-spinner Harbhajan Singh through the leg side and the ball clipped his pads. Slats didn't even bother looking up until suddenly he noticed the fielders were celebrating. As were the two umpires. Out lbw! Fortunately this decision wasn't all that costly for us (although some Bombay-based gambling syndicate must have paid out big) but it takes the lbw count so far this tour to 6–0 in their favour. Soon after that I joined Heals at the wicket in search of quick runs and some much-needed batting practice. We managed to push the score along and, despite a few mistimed shots, and a near run-out, I felt I was settling in well, despite the heat and quite bitter sledging. Now we all know a bit of 'verbal encouragement' is all part of the game and I can take whatever is dished out, but the abuse being directed at me was quite personal and vicious. To make matters worse, it was coming from Heals. (The near run-out may technically have been my fault.) Despite a few more dubious lbw decisions we managed to notch up 567 runs (Todd 73) before the match was called off thirty-five minutes early.

After the game there were naturally a few friendly drinks shared by both teams. The President's XI were keen to talk and learn from us and it was good chatting with the two or three players we allowed into our dressing room.

After the team meeting this evening (at which it was agreed we should all get back to the basics), Swampy made a surprise announcement that he would not be coming along as coach on our tour of Sharjah. This is because he's been hospitalised three times over there with asthma. We were naturally disappointed to hear the news but promised to pick him up a carton of duty-free Winfields on the way back home.

Even though we didn't actually win the match today we still enjoyed a few quiet ales back at the hotel. Some teams rarely do this but for us it's imperative to let off steam with a few drinks, a bit of dancing, a small party — really celebrate a victory. We celebrate losses in much the same way. And draws. And even rest days.

Day 12 ✌ (Tues March 3)

From Vizag to Chennai should have been a straightforward trip but of course nothing in India is ever really straightforward. At the airport we were met by the usual hordes of ever-hungry autograph hunters. Even after being ushered into a special lounge we were still beseiged. So a squadron of special airport security guards was summoned to protect us, heavily armed with guns, batons and, as it turned out, autograph books. With our plane's departure delayed for some unknown reason the only way we could relieve the boredom was by playing cards. (And sitting as far away from Tugga as possible.) Naturally enough we had one or two drinks to help pass the time and, eventually, our boarding call came. Unfortunately none of us heard it. Finally they closed the bar on us and we were forced to board. No sooner had I got on the plane than I found someone sitting in my seat. The little bastard refused to move and I was that close to demanding to speak with the pilot when Ponts pointed out this guy was the pilot. I don't remember much about the flight after this point.

Tubs and Tugga are both feeling a lot better today but our star leg-spinner Warney is starting to look a little thin. Problem is Warney can't stand the food on offer over here and has been living on a diet of stale potato chips, vanilla ice-cream and toast. As it happens, that's pretty much his normal diet at home, but he'd really like to add some baked beans or canned spaghetti for variety. A fax was duly sent to the ACB back in Australia and hopefully some decent food should arrive soon before the 'Sheik of Tweak' becomes nothing more than flab and bone.

After checking in to the hotel I phoned Ros and received some good news on the building front. The extensions are going well and the sun-room is now at lock-up stage. According to the contract we signed with

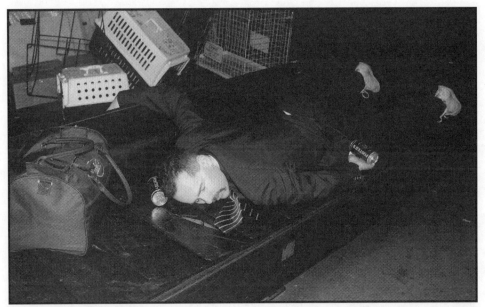

Arriving at Chennai airport.

Geeton Constructions it was supposed to be at this stage a week ago but Ros explained that Barry's been busier than he expected in the bedroom.

With the first Test just a few days away there's a lot of speculation over who will be in our final line-up. It looks like being a toss-up between Gavin 'Robbo' Robertson, Adam 'Chip'n' Dale and Paul 'Blocker' Wilson. Robbo is also known as 'the Riddler' and I think having two nicknames to choose from might just tip him in favour of selection. I know all three would desperately love a Test berth but waiting your turn is just part of the game, as I explained pushing past them at the buffet dinner tonight.

Day 13 ✌ (Wed March 4)

After breakfast this morning we headed down to the Chidambaram Stadium for yet another training session. The first thing that strikes you about this ground is the filthy creek that circles it. Known locally as the Buckingham Canal it's really nothing more than an open sewer and its foul stench is so bad as to be almost intolerable. I've not smelt anything so nauseating since I accidentally unzipped one of Mark Waugh's kit bags back at the hotel.

Returning here to Chennai (or Madras as it used to be known) brings back so many memories of that famous tied Test in '86, when Deano made his legendary double-century. It was scored in such appalling heat that by the second day Deano was being dragged into the showers, stripped naked and shoved under cold water, an experience he hadn't endured since his bucks party.

Our midfield training session allowed us to inspect the pitch which was mud-brown, hard and baked dry. As was lunch.

On the way back from the ground our bus travelled along the waterfront where we witnessed numerous games of cricket in progress. Kids of all ages, with little more than an old bat and a few sticks for stumps would be locked in battle. To see their innocent faces and wide-eyed smiles it was hard to imagine that many of them would grow up to become Hindu fundamentalists or Sikh terrorists hell-bent on widespread violence. It's a sobering thought.

An official function tonight — drinks with our tour sponsor Foster's — saw a good turn-up from the boys. Unfortunately it also saw a good turn-up from local autograph hunters, all desperate for that important scribble. Eventually security arrived and got rid of the gate-crashers so we could relax and enjoy our sponsor's product. I must say that with the first Test just a few days away security has been greatly improved.

It was hard to imagine that most of them would grow up to be terrorists.

Each night armed guards search our hotel corridors and surrounds, including every bush and even the rubbish bins, which is where they happened to find me lying face down shortly before dawn. I think you can be too supportive of a sponsor.

Day 14 ✌ (Thur March 5)

Our final training session before the first Test was excellent, with the entire squad attempting to simulate a match-day situation. Tubs was caught behind twice slashing outside off-stump, Junior and Slats were involved in a mid-wicket collision and Pistol even managed to pull a muscle, giving the whole morning a truly authentic feel.

Credit for this sort of intensity must go to our coach Swampy, who has always emphasised the need for solid training. Net sessions, fielding practice and general fitness work are all set up and supervised by him. Of course, when it comes to technical stuff he's perfectly willing to tap into the skills and expertise of other players. If someone is having problems hooking he'll get Ian Chappell in. If someone is struggling in slips he'll get Bob Simpson. And if he just wants a big night on the turps Greg Ritchie is rarely more than a phone call away.

Good news for Warney with word coming through that Heinz are sending over 2000 cans of baked beans. Not so good news for anyone rooming with him during the next month.

At the team meeting tonight (at which it was agreed we should get back to basics) it was announced Robbo would be in the team, making him the 375th player to represent Australia at Test level. He'll be presented with his cap before the match starts on Friday morning and then — as part of a long Aussie tradition — will be required to have the number 375 tattooed on his arse. It's a painful procedure having all three figures inscribed on your anatomy and I'm forever grateful that I was the 309th Australian Test player selected. All I needed was the 3 on one buttock and the 9 on the other — then it was just a question of bending over (see photo page 254).

The team meeting was followed by a traditional Test eve dinner, in

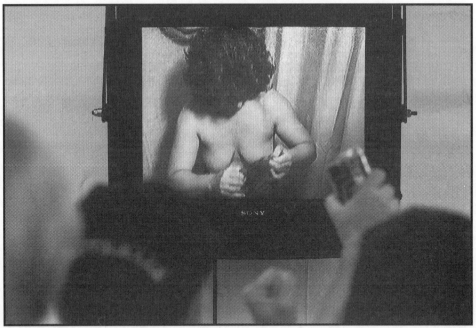

Motivational videos play a big part on tour.

which I ordered a pizza so large I could barely finish a third of it. How Warney knocked off two still amazes me.

After dinner Swampy showed us a motivational video which featured some golden moments from our past 18 months, followed by something involving Pamela Lee Anderson just to get the lads really fired up.

An interesting bit of cricket news from England was reported today in the *Hindu*. Apparently Debbie Lee, girlfriend of Aussie one-day player Stuart Law, walked into the members' pavilion at Lord's dressed only in her underwear. This was of course a protest against the MCC who just last week voted to maintain their ban on female members, the only exception of course being the Queen. (And Prince Edward.)

Day 15 ✌ (Fri Mar 6)

**First Test
India vs Australia, Day 1**

The morning of a Test match is always a busy one for me. Up early, showering, getting dressed, finding my way back to the team hotel. Then there's always a bundle of good-luck faxes from home to be sorted into piles — Warney's and the rest of the team's.

At breakfast I noticed our new boy Robbo was looking a little nervous. Hard to blame him really. Having played just one Shield match in three years and taken only one wicket so far on tour it's a pretty daunting task facing up to the likes of Tendulkar in front of a big crowd. As a senior player I know it's my job to put the new blokes at ease and I went over and had a quiet word with the young off-spinner. I simply told him all of Australia was behind him, he'd be bowling for his career, the team depended on him taking wickets and if he failed he'd be letting down himself, his colleagues and his country. I think it settled him down.

Down at the ground 30 000 fans had packed the MA Chidambaram Stadium, which wouldn't have been a problem except that about 29 000 of them seemed to be in our dressing room. Eventually the area was cleared and we were able to unpack our gear. A few of us senior players wandered outside for a quick inspection of the pitch (it was as dry and barren as Greg Matthews' scalp) before letting Tubby get on with the toss. Unfortunately he lost and, with the Indians electing to bat, we took to the field. I must say, walking out onto the ground the noise coming from the stands was almost deafening. Indian crowds really are amazing. They dance, bang drums, blow horns and whistles. It's hard to think of a word to describe it. 'Annoying' springs to mind.

Kaspa and Pistol opened proceedings with some tight bowling but despite this Mongia and Sidhu made steady progress. Pistol had Sidhu plumb lbw in the fifth over but hometown umpire Venkat refused to pay it. I was fielding in close and naturally a few good-natured 'pleasantries' were uttered when suddenly the Indian opener backed away from the crease and began complaining to the umpire that I'd called him a 'cheating a#$ehole', which was a total lie. Sure, I had used this phrase but I was referring to Umpire Venkat, not the batsman. Eventually play resumed, with the Indians making it to lunch at 0 for 86. Things were looking grim; not only was the game in danger of slipping away from us, the chicken tikka was as tough as nails.

After lunch Sidhu was on 58 when he edged one from Warney which then touched Heal's gloves before deflecting to Tubs at first slip who grassed it. It was a sharp chance but I could tell our skipper was pretty disappointed with himself, as were we. Everyone in the team has received the old Tubby Taylor 'death stare' at one time or another for minor misdemeanours — dropping a catch or misfielding a ball. Or in my case, crashing the team bus. We all know what it's like and were happy to return the favour. Fortunately for Tubs, Sidhu only made another 4 runs before being dismissed, paving the way for the long-awaited Warne vs Tendulkar clash. Round one went to Warney, who dismissed the cocky little curry-muncher for just 4 runs. More tight bowling and fielding saw the Indians reach stumps at 5 for 232, a good fight-back from us all.

One of the finest batsmen in the world. And Mongia.

33

Day 16 ✌ (Sat Mar 7)

First Test
India vs Australia, Day 2

Looking out the window this morning my heart sank at the sight of another clear blue sky and fierce sun beating down. And the team bus just pulling out of the hotel car park. Bloody wake-up call must not have come through. I eventually managed to get dressed and grab a taxi (though not exactly in that order) and arrived at the ground in time to take the field.

Warney and Robbo bowled sensational spells, taking five more wickets between them, knocking the home team over for just 257. The only negative was Blewie being hit in the knee from a Dravid sweep shot. He hobbled off the ground and was distressed to hear he may now have to bat further down the order. But as I commented to him, it's probably where he belongs anyway.

As we prepared to commence our innings there was a mood of tension in the Australian dressing room. This was a big match and would likely set the tone for the rest of the series. But as always our skipper Tubby Taylor was keeping cool. This is one of Tubs' great strengths: no matter how much pressure he might be under personally he stays calm, issuing instructions and advice to the team. Sometimes it's a little hard to hear him from behind the cubicle door but that's only a minor problem.

I couldn't help but notice that Tugga had decided to occupy the same chair Deano sat in after his famous double century here in '86. The chair has remained untouched since that match and our vice-captain no doubt hoped some good luck might rub off. Unfortunately all that appeared to rub off was a nasty-looking stain.

One man looking more than a little pensive was Slats, padding up to face his first ball in Test cricket in sixteen months. It was here in India that an ill-advised slash outside off-stump cost him a place in the team. Of course, putting such thoughts and memories out of your mind is all part of being a professional sportsman and everyone wished the talented New South Welshman good luck as he walked out the door. 'Nothing stupid outside off!' I good-naturedly quipped at the departing opener. He was out for 11 runs. At the other end Tubs was having to contend with the fierce spin of Kumble. He reached 12 before getting an edge to the keeper.

Tubs celebrates reaching double figures.

Ponts fell for 18 on the last ball before tea. The young Tasmanian was obviously not happy with the decision and stood his ground for quite some time before departing. This was a foolish thing to do: not only did he display bad sportsmanship, he took so long returning to the rooms that someone ate his biscuits.

After tea I went in to bat and struggled a little early — possibly too many biscuits. But I eventually found my rhythm and was looking set for a big score when I was given out 'off the glove' by Umpire Venkat. It was a shocking decision but I wasn't about to repeat Ponts' behaviour and stand my ground. Instead I stormed right up to the incompetent fool and indicated exactly which part of my *shoulder* the ball had hit. But the decision was made and I eventually departed the ground.

We finished the day at 7 for 193 (still 65 runs behind) with Heals unbeaten and looking in good touch. Though none of us made a really big score we were all out in the middle long enough to learn something about batting here in India. Play late, watch the ball and don't call Umpire Venkat a 'short-sighted curry-munching cheat'. Apparently I'm seeing the match referee tomorrow.

Day 17 ✌ (Sun Mar 8)

First Test
India vs Australia, Day 3

Despite the hotel room air-conditioner running at full blast I still woke up this morning in a pool of sweat. Turned out my electric blanket had been switched to high, a late-night practical joke courtesy no doubt of Messers Ponting and Waugh.

Down at the ground there was another massive crowd, due partly — we were informed — to some religious holiday. Honestly, these people are worse than the Jews!*

Heals and Warney went out to resume our innings but the blond leg-spinning sensation (his description, not mine) was out just a few balls later. That's when Robbo joined our keeper for a record ninth wicket stand of 96 runs. The nuggety Queenslander was unlucky not to reach his century, falling short on 90, but the four hours he spent at the crease were pure Heals. We were eventually all out for 328, a lead of 71 runs. During the tea interval our skipper (whose edge to the keeper for 12 was pure Tubs) spoke about the need to capitalise on this lead with early wickets in the final session.

The Indian openers got away to a good start but then Mongia was given out lbw to Blewie. Not surprisingly the decision came from independent umpire George Sharp but you could tell the batsman was not happy. Naturally we took great pleasure in directing him to the showers. A few more heated exchanges took place as Sidhu dispatched successive

*My publisher wanted me to make it clear that there is nothing racist intended by this remark. In saying Indian people are worse than the Jews I am merely making a reference to the large number of religious holidays both cultures tend to celebrate. As far as *people* go, obviously Jews are far worse. I hope that's cleared things up.

The festivities were kept pretty low-key.

balls from Warney to the boundary but the cocky little opener seemed untroubled by our comments. It was then we realised what was going on. The bloke doesn't speak English! Frankly, I think this borders on cheating, not being capable of understanding a few well-chosen remarks from the fielders around you. It's certainly something the match referee should look into and I might just raise it the next time I'm summoned to appear before him. Anyway, the home team made it to stumps without losing a further wicket.

Naturally there were a few celebrations in our room after play with Heals' magnificent 90 and Robbo's debut 57 both receiving warm applause. But with another two days still to play the festivities were kept pretty low-key and we all headed back to the hotel for an early night.

Day 18 ✌ (Mon Mar 9)

First Test
India vs Australia, Day 4

No matter how long I stay in India I will never get over the passion for cricket these people have. Everyone you meet seems to know all about you. Certainly the police officer who arrested me outside the Taj Coromandel at 2.30 am this morning did. Fortunately I was able to 'escape' the long arm of the law in return for the mandatory signature and a souvenir cap.

By Day Four of a Test the Australian dressing room tends to look like a bomb has hit it. There's gear everywhere, empty drink containers, players jostling for a position near the air-conditioner. And with just a few minutes to go before play the mood is tense. Our bowlers know we need quick wickets, Tubs desperately wants a win, Tugga can't find his Australian cap. It's pressure cooker stuff.

An early wicket saw India at 2 for 44 and looking vulnerable when Tendulkar strode to the crease. Put simply, he tore us apart: 191 balls, 4 sixes and 14 fours in a total of 155 not out. Warney tried everything: changing ends, switching from over to round the wicket, extra grunting. But the twenty-five year old, considered by many to be the best batsman in the world, kept piling on the runs. Not that he was the Lone Ranger in this department. Sidhu, Dravid and Azharuddin all made half centuries as well before the home side declared at 4 for 418, a lead of 348 runs.

During the tea break Swampy spoke about the need to concentrate and not lose any wickets in the final session. It was an inspiring speech but unfortunately Slats, Tubby and Blewie must not have heard him, as they all fell cheaply in the first ten overs. Perhaps the most disheartening wicket was that of Tubby, who fell for 13 off the very last ball of the day. To see his face as he trudged off the ground you could tell he was very upset with himself and would probably not feel like talking to anyone for quite some time. So out of respect we all decided to jump on the bus and let him walk home. At 3 for 31 and still a long way behind we'll have to pull out something very special if we are to save this match tomorrow.

The only real positive news from today was that cocky Indian wicketkeeper Nayan Mongia has been charged with dissent following his lbw dismissal yesterday and must now face match referee Peter van der Merwe tonight. It's about time these Indian

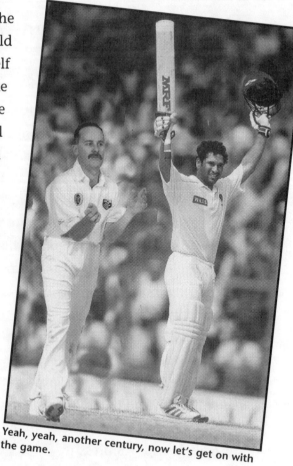

Yeah, yeah, another century, now let's get on with the game.

players were taught a thing or two about good sportsmanship and I intend making that very point when I face the referee at my hearing tomorrow.

Day 19 ✌ (Tues Mar 10)

First Test
Umpire S Venkatraghavan vs Australia, Day 5

It was always going to be difficult surviving an entire day in the field against a pumped-up Indian attack but our task was made no easier by several controversial (i.e. sh*#house) umpiring decisions. The first to suffer was Junior who had reached 18 when he was adjudged caught by a ball that clearly came off his pads. Then Ponts suffered a similar fate, being given lbw to a ball that obviously hit his bat. To be fair, the crowd noise was at its deafening peak meaning that the umpires were forced to rely solely on their eyes rather than their ears. Even watching a replay of the Ponting dismissal in our dressing room we struggled to hear a 'snick'. Mind you, Slats had Bon Jovi turned up pretty loud on the ghetto-blaster at this stage. Tugga and I tried hard to halt the momentum but the umpires were obviously keen on an early lunch. Tugga was given out 'caught' off Raju and suddenly it was up to me and Heals to salvage something from the innings. We managed to push the score along slowly but mere survival was the order of the day. It wasn't just the Indian bowling and umpiring that made things difficult, the heat and humidity were equally appalling. In temperatures of 42 degrees and with humidity hovering round 89 per cent it's crucial to preserve energy. You can't take off for quick singles like Dean Jones. You've got to walk or sometimes not move at all and wait for a boundary. Boonie was an expert at this technique, undergoing as little physical exertion as possible in order to beat the heat. He'd do it even when playing in Hobart. But if Australia looked like saving the match those umpires had other ideas. This time it was Umpire George Sharp who declared that Todd was out 'bat before wicket'.

Naturally I was disappointed and queried the umpire as I departed the pitch. But the decision had been made and there was nothing to do but head for the dressing room, which is where I think my bat had landed a few minutes earlier. From there we sat and watched as the remaining boys were dismissed. All out for 168, giving India victory by 179 runs.

Understandably it was a rather sombre scene in the Aussie rooms after the match. But there's no point in crying over spilt milk and pretty soon the old ghetto-blaster was cranked up as the boys drowned their sorrows with a few cold beers. In my opinion this has always been one of the strengths of Australian cricket: whenever countries like India or Pakistan lose a match the post mortems go on forever, with fingers

There's a pretty fine line between dissent and disappointment.

being pointed and players attacked. We simply accepted the loss, blamed the umpires and got on with the job at hand. Drinking. Naturally a few of us senior players visited the Indian rooms to offer our congratulations. This is something a lot of people have difficulty understanding; how you can spend five days locked in heated battle on a cricket ground and then sit down together for some friendly drinks. The answer lies in the old adage, 'What happens on the field stays on the field.' Chatting over a few beers is a great way of putting aside cultural or racial differences and bringing blokes closer together. They're not a bad bunch the Indians — friendly, good-natured, polite. Close your eyes and they could almost be white.

To end a pretty disappointing day I was informed back at the hotel that I had been reported to the match referee for showing 'dissent' after my laughable lbw dismissal. What really hurts is that Ponts, who spoke to the umpire exactly like I did, has somehow evaded any disciplinary action. According to the umpire, all Ponts did was show 'disappointment', rather than 'dissent'. If you ask me, there's a pretty fine line between the two.

Day 20 ✌ (Wed Mar 11)

Travel in India is never a straightforward matter and today once again proved that point. The plan was we would fly to Jamshedpur aboard a chartered flight for our next three-day tour match against India A. But having sat at the airport cocktail lounge for over three hours we were eventually informed that our plane would not be arriving. Some idiot in a safari suit from the Board of Control for Cricket then suggested we catch the train but as the trip involved a journey of over 200 kilometres our team manager 'Brute' Bernard put his foot down. Either get us a plane or you can stick the match up your collective arses. Of course, Brute knows the importance of diplomacy in these situations and never actually uttered those rather blunt words. But I did. (You've gotta lay down the law for these turban-wearing twerps or they'll walk all over you.) In the end it was agreed that 1) a flight would be arranged for tomorrow, 2) I'd write a letter of apology to the Indian Board of Control, and 3) they'd stop serving me bourbon and Coke.

With a free day now to fill most of the guys took the opportunity to relax back at the hotel. Walking the streets was not really an option due to the ever-present autograph hunters so it was a question of grabbing some sleep or attending the team meeting. In the end I managed to do both simultaneously.

Chatting with Swampy this evening he mentioned the possibility of resting Warney for this next game. I must say the Test really took it out of our number one bowler. To see him between overs the other day, bent over, hands on knees, gasping for air. It reminded me of the time he last went for a jog. Speaking of Warney, news came through today that he has been offered $50 000 to promote Heinz baked beans. It's obviously a tempting offer but as I said to him, 'Think about it carefully mate. The cash may be good but we cricketers have an image to uphold and must be very selective about which products we lend our name to over here.'

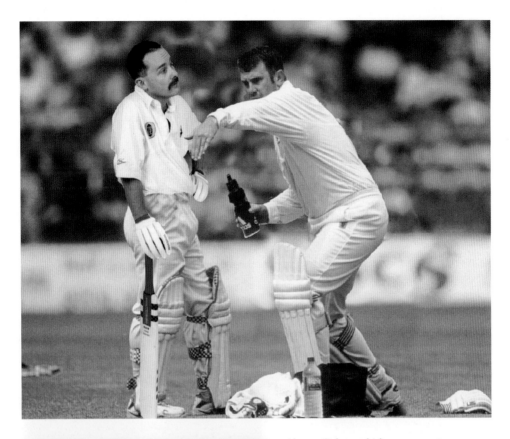

Above: Tubs and I have a great relationship. He often gives me batting advice. And I often pretend to listen.

Left: As a golfer he plays off 7, which — coincidentally — is his current tour average.

Warwick Todd

My first car.

Our wedding day.

A proud dad.

Grandpa Todd is laid to rest.

Above: Our one-day matches were often marred by objects being thrown onto the pitch.

Left: As it turned out, most of them were thrown by Aussie fans over here on a supporters' tour.

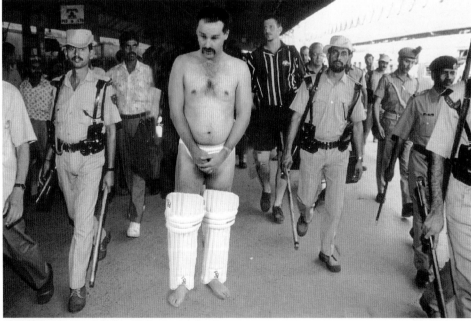

Some days are simply best left unexplained.

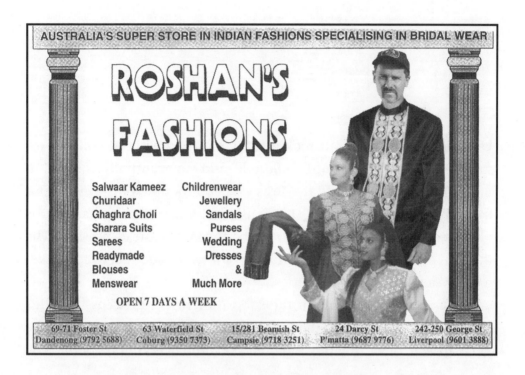
Spending another night in Chennai didn't really bother me and quite a few of the younger blokes were rather pleased as they'd picked up a few female 'fans' during the match and were keen to continue 'fraternising'. A lot of people find it hard to believe but no matter where we Aussies tour in the world there are always young ladies of the female persuasion keen on 'getting close' to their heroes. Of course, those of us who are married or nursing groin injuries tend to avoid such 'activities'* but it's not always easy to fend off admiring fans. Even fielding down on the boundary you get all sorts of things said to you, women handing you their phone numbers, that sort of thing. I remember once playing at Lord's, I was fielding on the fence when this raucous chick, obviously a little tipsy, yelled out 'hey Toddy, turn round and I'll show you my tits!' In the end I did and she did! The Duchess and I have remained good friends ever since.

---

* I've used a lot of 'quotation marks' here to avoid offending any delicate readers who'd rather not see the word 'rooting'.

Day 21 ✌ (Thur Mar 12)

Our flight to Jamshedpur took off this morning without incident (or safety features, from what I could tell) and we eventually checked in at the Tata Guesthouse. In the Tests we get a room to ourselves but for the other games it's twin share. I'm rooming with Slats and as always our first job was to push the beds as far apart as possible. The thought of actually touching another bloke, even accidentally, makes me physically sick.

Making phone calls from the subcontinent is never easy but this afternoon I managed to get a line out and speak with Ros. She and the kids are well, obviously missing their dad, and everything's going well

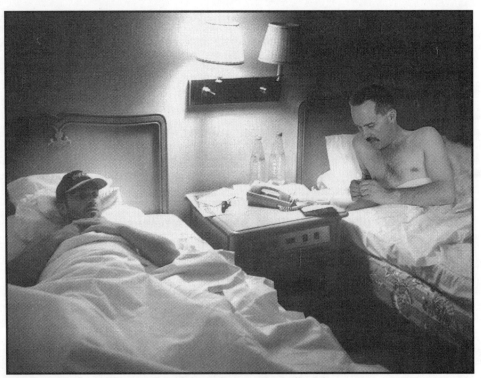

The thought of touching another bloke makes me physically sick.

on the extension front, which is good news. I was a little worried Geeton Constructions might not have been the best choice of builders but from what Ros says she's really been pleased by Barry. We could have chatted for ages but I was mindful of the high cost of international calls from India, especially as I'd snuck into Swampy Marsh's room while he was out to use the phone.

At the team meeting tonight we spoke about many things including Tubby's continued lack of form. It was a good opportunity for everyone to have a say and the discussion was surprisingly frank. Until Tubby arrived unexpectedly and we all pretty much shut up. The team for tomorrow was announced, with quite a few of the new blokes like Boof, Blocker, Magilla and Chip'n all getting a run. Swampy then spoke about the need for maintaining match fitness throughout the coming weeks. It was a good speech but thankfully also a short one, which allowed us to make the hotel's happy hour without missing too many drinks.

Like most places in India Jamshedpur offers very little in the way of night-life or entertainment, so when the head honcho of Tata Steel invited us all to his place for a barbecue there were quite a few takers. Normally of course these sorts of semi-official functions are about as popular as training but team management put the hard word on us to attend. As usual it was a total bore, just another rich bloke showing off his mansion. Reminded me of a team dinner we once had at Warney's place. At least the food was good and the beer was cold. And it was a pretty swish house. The guy had antiques and amazing Indian works of art on just about every wall. God knows what some of them would be worth. (Guess I'll have to wait until I get home to have the statue I pinched valued.)

Day 22 ✌ (Fri Mar 13)

India A vs Australia, Day 1

Another early wake-up call saw the boys heading bleary-eyed down to breakfast. The food was again appalling: stale cereal, cold scrambled eggs and toast so hard it tasted like someone had just cut out a square of cardboard and covered it in jam. Which is exactly what Messrs Reiffel and Waugh (M) had done. Worst part is, I ordered an extra slice.

Down at the Keenan Stadium overnight rain and poor light combined to delay play for several hours. As we arrived the ground staff were out trying to dry the ground with a Super Sopa. This is an amazing piece of equipment that can literally 'soak' up 1000 litres an hour. It's known to us Aussies as a 'Boonie'. Even without play there's always plenty to do in the Australian rooms and this morning we were faced with a veritable mountain of bats awaiting team signatures. Now all of us recognise just how much a collection of autographed willows can mean to an ex-Test player celebrating his testimonial year or a Shield cricketer struggling to supplement a meagre income, but after signing over 200 bats we discovered they were for our bus driver's brother-in-law who runs a sports store in Bombay. I think that might be crossing the line.

Eventually the sun broke through and India A won the toss, electing to bat. You could feel the competitive tension between Magilla, Blocker and Chip'n as all three were clearly bowling for a place in the Test team. The giveaway was how they kept coming up to each other and saying 'good luck mate'. Australian cricketers never say 'Good luck' to someone unless we want them to fail.

On yet another flat pitch the Indian A openers looked a little ruffled as they poked and prodded through the first fifteen overs. Just when our bowlers were switching into top gear the umpires decided the light was too poor and offered the batsmen the choice of going off. Which naturally the spineless little bastards did, scurrying for the boundary as if a cyclone was brewing. Honestly, there would have been two clouds in the sky! The only reason I would have left the field was for more sunscreen. Anyway, the little weasels were eventually flushed out after twenty minutes or so and play resumed. Blocker and Magilla both picked up two wickets to have the home team 4 for 92 at lunch.

The afternoon session was a good one, with some more tight bowling from Pistol and the new boys. Unfortunately the day was marred by an incident involving myself and a catch off middle order batsman Amay Khurasia. What happened was Blocker pitched one up, the batsman got an edge and I took a pretty smart catch in the gully, diving to my right and rolling several times before holding the prized red cherry aloft. So naturally I was rather disappointed to see the

Tubs pointing out where he'd like to see me fielding.

batsman refusing to walk. The umpires then came over, along with the Aussie slips cordon, and a fairly heated discussion took place during which I was accused of cheating. I've got to say, having your professional integrity and good name questioned by the opposition is pretty hard to take. But when it's your own captain making the claim it really hurts.

The home team made it through to stumps with only one more wicket falling. After play we all enjoyed a few quiet drinks in the rooms as the sun set over Jamshedpur. Winding down after a long day in the field is important and we all have different ways of doing it. A few drinks, a game of cards, a rub-down. Some of the younger blokes even shower, but personally I think that's going a bit far.

Day 23 ✌ (Sat Mar 14)

India A vs Australia, Day 2

Overnight rain again delayed the start of play, this time for almost three hours. When we finally got onto the field our bowlers did the job, taking four quick wickets to leave the home team 9 for 216 (declared).

Pick of our bowlers was no doubt Blocker Wilson, who ended up with four wickets, showing plenty of early promise. All that really stands between him and Test selection now is his beard.

Blocker's beard — simply not up to Test standard...

After the usual break Tubs and Slats went out to open the innings, all of us wishing our skipper good luck. As it turned out, Tubs looked in fine form, racing along to a solid half-century. After he departed Blewie and Tugga put together a great partnership and by stumps we'd passed the India A total for the loss of just three wickets, making it a pretty good day for the team. Marred by only one incident. After the match a group of local 'journalists' came into our room for an interview. I say 'journalists' because I think the term is used a little loosely over here. Basically, anyone who owns a pen and wants to barge into the Australian dressing room seems to qualify. Anyway, we were happy to let them ask a few questions, it's a chance for the younger guys to learn how to handle an interview. After the usual 'Are you enjoying the tour?', 'Do you think you can win the second Test?', 'How's Warney's shoulder?' stuff, they announced they'd like to present us with a locally made rug. Naturally there was a photo involved and while we were all sitting there pretending to look grateful one of them, a short bloke in a turban, started giving us advice on how to look after the rug. He told us we should take it outside at least once a year and beat it. To which I replied, 'Just like you guys do with your wives!' I don't think it went down all that well as they all left soon after. (Hopefully they'll realise it was a harmless joke.)

CRICKET: INDIA VS AUSTRALIA TOUR UPDATE

Racial Slur Sours Aussie Tour

■ *By Kirumundi Tekkarmudi*

RELATIONS between India and Australia hit an all-time low yesterday when visiting Australian batsman Warwick Todd (pictured) made an offensive remark about Hindu marriages. Speaking in the Australian dressing room Todd claimed that domestic violence was an accepted part of Indian culture. Todd also offended religious sensitivities by suggesting "You blokes should eat more beef" before being gagged by a clearly embarrassed team management. *(Continued page 3)*

Day 24 ✌ (Sun Mar 15)

India A vs Australia, Day 3

More sickness worries for the team today, with Adam 'Chip'n' Dale unable to take the field courtesy of a stomach bug (much to the amusement of the lads). No one is quite sure what he might have eaten but we all had an extra nip of whisky at breakfast as a precautionary measure.

With the tour match looking set to fizzle out into a tame draw it was hard mustering much enthusiasm but those of us sitting in the dressing room certainly gave Tugga's 107 a warm round of applause when someone interrupted our card game to tell us about it. My innings was disappointing, caught behind for just 12, after making the fundamental error of planning my next shot before the ball was bowled. You'll always get in trouble premeditating and the annoying thing was I knew I was going to do it. To make matters worse, after returning to the rooms I was informed the ACB had lodged an official complaint about my bat. Now, as an experienced first class cricketer I appreciate there are restrictions on what players may advertise out on the field but I honestly couldn't believe anyone could have a problem with the subtle sponsorship message my bat displayed.

We eventually made it to 391 (a lead of 175) and the home team commenced their second innings. Magilla picked up a few early wickets but you could tell the match was heading for a tame draw. Sure enough, towards the end Heals handed his gloves over to Ponts, Tubby had a bowl and we even put Pistol in a catching position.

With the game eventually called off we all gathered for a few quiet drinks. Sharing a beer and a few laughs after a match is, in my opinion, a marvellous way of bringing players together and the spirit in the

I honestly couldn't believe anyone could have a problem with the subtle sponsorship message my bat displayed.

rooms was really good. Until the Indian players arrived and things got a little boring. I was stuck for half an hour in conversation with a bloke called Anathapadmanabhan. All I kept thinking was, 'How does this fella go signing 200 bats for a sponsor?' (I've always envied Glenn 'Pigeon' McGrath in this respect — all he's expected to do is mark the bat with an X.)

Eventually we got rid of the home team (told 'em we had a team meeting) and went back to the hotel for a meal and a few drinks. After this most of the lads gathered in Brute Bernard's room for a video night, featuring a few R-rated blue-ies someone must have smuggled in. You certainly can't get these sorts of films here — the Indian's idea of full-frontal nudity is a chick not wearing a veil. Anyway, the boys all enjoyed themselves, especially the younger blokes. Of course, being a married man myself it was all nothing I hadn't seen before. Though not for quite some time.

Day 25 ✌ (Mon Mar 16)

The trip to Calcutta this morning was intended to be by charter flight but somehow we ended up on a bus. According to our driver it was a 'deluxe' model (meaning it had brakes) but even so we managed to break down during the short journey more often than Craig McDermott on an overseas tour.

Eventually we reached the 'City of Joy', which was covered in its trademark smog and haze. Yet the heat and humidity were quite low and I decided to risk a short walk round the town. Big mistake. Within a few hundred metres of the team hotel I was mobbed by desperate autograph-hunters and forced to beat a hasty retreat. Yet even back inside the Taj Bengal the lobby was full of even more dishevelled, raucous crowds all jostling to get close and waving notepads. Pushing through this smelly mass of unwashed flesh I wondered how the Australian press contingent always seem to know where we are staying.

The Australian team bus. This was the 'deluxe' model.

After settling in and having lunch we visited the famous Eden Gardens ground, venue for the second Test. According to the papers 60 000 are expected here tomorrow — and that's just to watch the pitch being prepared. There's no doubt they love their cricket here in Calcutta and 80 000 are expected on Wednesday, with many fans having saved all year to afford the 200 rupee (about $4) entrance fee for the cheapest seats, which tend to be either way up the back or on fire.

It's an old team tradition that two nights before a Test the whole squad goes out for dinner. It used to be the night before a Test but back in '95 a few players were breathalyzed driving to the MCG for the Boxing Day Test, so it was pushed back a day to give everyone a chance to recover. Sharing a meal is a marvellous way of bringing the boys together and boosting team morale and there's no discrimination between senior and junior players. The younger blokes are free to come over and join the senior table any time they feel like it, provided they don't hang round too long, or expect to be included in the conversation.

The final team for the second Test won't be announced until tomorrow but there was a lot of speculation as to who would line up in two days' time. On the bowling front there's a feeling we should go in with three spinners which could mean that Magilla replaces Pistol. As for our batting line-up, Blewie is vulnerable, especially with his South Australian team-mate Boof making 76 in Jamshedpur. Situations like this, with two blokes fighting for the one position can sometimes turn ugly but it's a credit to Blewie and Boof that I am yet to hear an angry or terse word exchanged between the two. In fact, I am yet to hear any words exchanged, they haven't spoken to each other since leaving Sydney.

Day 26 ✌ (Tues Mar 17)

The day before a Test match is always a hectic one with so much to be achieved in so little time. There was no way I was ever going to fit in net practice, a shave, a haircut and a massage and naturally something had to go. I would have liked a hit in the nets but I guess learning to compromise is just part of being an Australian cricketer.

Our fast-bowling stocks hit an all-time low this morning with Pistol's shoulder breaking down. It's his right shoulder which has become inflamed from the relentless grind of constant bowling. This comes as a real disappointment for Pistol, not to mention myself as I had just bet $200 at odds of 30 to 1 that he wouldn't take a wicket for the match. According to the ACB press release, Pistol will have a week of intensive treatment after which 'his future will be reassessed'. Translation: They're still trying to find a ticket on the next flight out of Calcutta.

It rained this afternoon, as it has for the past few days, and I decided to take a walk round town, just to settle a few nerves and get the feel of the place. I tell you, if you ever need reminding just how good we've got it back in Australia, spend a few hours wandering through the slums of Calcutta. There were people living in tin shacks that I wouldn't keep a dog in. (Certainly not since the RSPCA slapped a cruelty charge on the Warwick Todd Boarding Kennels back in 1993. As part of the court order Ros and I are no longer allowed to keep animals of any sort.) As well as the substandard housing there were beggars just about everywhere. They'd look up at you with those big brown eyes, imploring you to hand over a few rupees. Which normally I'd be happy to do but not one of them could provide a receipt. What's the point of charity if it's not tax deductible?

At the team meeting tonight Tubs finally announced the squad for tomorrow's match with no real surprises. Slats and Blewie held their spots while Blocker and Magilla have both been named to replace Pistol. Which of them plays will depend on an early morning pitch inspection. Swampy and Tubs then spoke about tactics for tomorrow's vital second Test. They went through each of the Indian players in turn, analysing their strengths and weaknesses, in particular areas we might be able to target. For example, their captain Azharuddin is a Muslim and therefore doesn't drink. It's not exactly a technical fault and we may have trouble exploiting it on field but we'll certainly be

able to get stuck into him in the dressing room after play. Then we broke into two groups, batsmen and bowlers, and discussed individual game plans. After that all the boys got together again and listened to Tubs, who had some good advice regarding the match tomorrow. Our skipper told us, 'You've got to know when to hold them, know when to fold them, know when to walk away and know when to run.' It was the first time we'd held a team meeting at a karaoke bar but judging from the response (Tugga even had a tear in his eye) it won't be the last.

It was the first time we'd held a team meeting at a karaoke bar.

Day 27 ✌ (Wed Mar 18)

2nd Test
India vs Australia, Day 1

The morning of a big Test match is always a busy one for W Todd. There's generally a bunch of good-luck faxes and letters that have to be sorted through and passed onto Warney before we all have breakfast, board the team bus and head for the ground. On the first day of a Test we like to get there at least fifteen minutes earlier than normal just to give ourselves time to prepare. Put gear away, sort out the seating, make sure the fridge is plugged in. Then of course there's the team warm-up, which we take very seriously.

The team warm-up, which we take very seriously.

They were predicting a crowd of 80 000 here today and judging from the noise as we walked out onto the ground for a pitch inspection this estimate seemed pretty accurate. The roar was deafening, it seemed like everyone in the stands was holding a trumpet or bugle or whistle or drum. Five minutes in the middle and we were desperate to reach the tranquillity of the dressing room. Until Tugga put his new John Williamson CD on, at which point the outside noise sounded a little more attractive.

Blocker was named in the team with Magilla becoming 12th man. The big leg-spinner was obviously pretty disappointed on missing out so I went over and had a quiet word with him about how important the 12th man role is and how he was a dead cert to play next match. I think he bought it.

Tubs won the toss and we elected to bat, with Slats and our skipper heading out to open the innings. Slats went fifth ball for a duck, followed next ball by Blewie. Then we lost Tubs for 3. Before the match our skipper had been quoted as saying of Eden Gardens, 'You just want to be able to say that you played here.' As it turned out, he played and missed here. When Junior went for 10, things were looking pretty desperate and I went out knowing a big innings was needed. Unfortunately Srinath had other ideas and got one to nip back, taking an edge and going straight to first slip. Todd out, 5. It was a long walk back to the rooms. And I tell you, I was so disappointed with myself it took me ages to leave the dressing room and go up to join my team-mates in the viewing area. In hindsight, setting fire to the stairs was possibly an overreaction, but I wanted to express my anger and Slats had already taken out all the windows.

Highlight of the day was the magnificent innings of Tugga who made 80, despite battling a groin strain that necessitated pain-killers and a runner. Tugga was eventually run out by his runner Blewie who then suffered a groin injury of his own, courtesy of our none too happy vice-captain. Ponts chipped in with a handy 60 but the damage had been done and by stumps we were all out for 233.

Things were very quiet in the Australian dressing room after play. Probably because we were back at the hotel enjoying a sponsor's function. There's no point moping over a poor performance. And, as Swampy said (just before tripping over a bar stool), we should always focus on the positives. Which, looking back over the day, were Tugga's 80 and lunch (excellent food and good-sized servings).

Day 28 ✌ (Thur Mar 19)

2nd Test
India vs Australia, Day 2

More injury worries for the team this morning with at least six squad members sidelined by hangovers. Personally I think our tour sponsor Foster's must share some of the blame, continuing to make their product available when it was obvious certain players had had enough. Those kegs should have been locked away, not left lying round in a storeroom where anyone determined enough could climb on Ricky Ponting's shoulders, force open a window with a cricket stump and get to them.

Down at the ground there were 78 000 fans waiting (2000 fewer than yesterday, but obviously that family had seen enough). After a few quick words from Tubs we took to the field determined for even quicker wickets. But the Indians had other ideas, tearing our bowling attack apart with an opening partnership of 191. Kaspa, Blocker, Blewie, Junior, Robbo and Warney were all belted about the park and there was little Tubs could do about it. He shuffled the field constantly, bringing blokes in close, pushing them onto the boundary, demanding I come back out of the rooms (what's a 12th man for if you can't use them during the odd personal drinks break?), but the home team continued their run feast.

Our biggest headache early on was opener Navjot Sidhu who, at 34 years of age, is the world's longest serving cricketer. We'd worked out a careful plan for the Punjabi pinch-hitter based not so much on his batting technique but on the fact that he was involved in a road rage killing some years ago. Those of us in the slips kept up a steady stream of automotive-based 'pleasantries' on this subject but the guy seemed unflappable. He went on to make 97, while his 'partner' (and we also tried this tack verbally) notched up 95. Shortly before tea a massive roar from the crowd went up, signalling only one thing — Tendulkar. Or another row of seats set on fire. Unfortunately it was Tendulkar and he continued the attack, racing along to 79 before slicing Kaspa to Blewie at point. It was a great innings and at one point the scoreboard flashed 'Sachin's tandoori is hotter than Shane's sandwiches', proving once again Indians have f*#k-all sense of humour. Mind you, it's always nice to have one's achievements acknowledged by the ground staff and it took me back to a very special afternoon at the MCG many years ago.

To make matters worse, Blocker left the field in the first hour with a strained lower abdomen, forcing Blewie to share the new ball with Kaspa. On top of that, Tugga spent the entire day in the dressing room receiving treatment on the groin injury he sustained yesterday. We really missed our vice-captain, not so much for his bowling but his unique ability in the area of psychological warfare. We were so short-

A proud moment at the MCG.

staffed in this area that at one point Kaspa was even called on to mutter a few 'compliments' in Tendulkar's direction. The best our paceman could come up with was 'You big dummy', a comment that I don't think exactly unsettled the master Indian strokeplayer. (I would have gone for 'You short-arsed poofter' but then again, I've had eleven years' first class experience.)

At stumps India were 3 for 369, a lead of 146, and as a team we were staring down the barrel of our most humiliating defeat since last November when we tried taking on the Australian Cricket Board.

Day 29 ✌ (Fri Mar 20)

2nd Test
India vs Australia, Day 3

Naturally the local press have had a field day overnight with our poor showing so far in this Test. We woke this morning to a series of predictable headlines like 'Aussies Outclassed', 'India Set for Win' and 'Todd Charged Over Restaurant Fight'. It's so easy for the alleged 'experts' to sit back in their air-conditioned commentary boxes criticising our performance but you have to bear in mind that because of injuries we're struggling to field 11 fit players. And one of those is Warney, so it's really closer to ten.

But, as the noble bard* himself once said, 'When the going gets tough the tough get going', and the mood was positive when we took to the ground this morning. Tubs set the most attacking field he could: three on the off, four on the onside and five in the dressing room receiving treatment from Hooter. Unfortunately the Indians had no intention of collapsing at this point and went on to post their highest ever score against Australia. Leading the charge was skipper Azharuddin, who defied everything we threw at him — from leg spin to anti-Islamic remarks — to notch up an unbeaten 163. On a positive note, our fielding improved dramatically compared to yesterday when at least 25 runs were conceded due to sloppy work. There's no point naming names here but obviously Messers Wilson, Warne, McGill (sub) and Ponting had a long hard look at themselves last night. Today's fielding was excellent and despite the heat everyone was alert and moved quickly. We practically sprinted off the field at lunch.

* Max Walker

India eventually declared during the tea break at 5 for 633, a lead of 400. Obviously we can't win the match from here but it can still be saved. The key was surviving the final session without losing a wicket. But it was not to be, with Slats dragging one back onto his leg stump in the fifth over. Out for just 5. Watching the young New South Welshman trudge off

Having hit rock bottom there's now only one way for Slats to go: New South Wales district cricket.

we all felt sorry for him, as you do for any cricketer going through such a horror stretch. The one consolation is that, having hit rock bottom there's now only one way for Slats to go: New South Wales district cricket.

We eventually made it through to stumps at 1 for 38, still facing a huge run chase just to make the home team bat again. It was quite a day of records, not only India's highest total against us but also Warney's all-time worst bowling figures of 0 for 147. Our blond leggie seemed pretty upset when he learnt of this and perhaps in hindsight I shouldn't have announced it during our team dinner. It was just something I felt everyone would like to know.

Back at the hotel there was good news and bad news. The bad — our planned casino night had been postponed because someone pinched the roulette wheel from Junior's room. The good news is that Victorian paceman Damien Fleming is being rushed to India to replace the injured Blocker and Pistol and should be here tomorrow. Apparently Flem was summoned by the selectors at 10.00 yesterday and told, 'You've got just three hours to pack your bags.' I've lost count of the number of times tour selectors have told me those very words.

Day 30 ✌ 🐌 (Sat Mar 21)

2nd Test
India vs Australia, Day 4

There's no point beating round the bush. We were rolled today, crushed, defeated, all out for a paltry 181. The collapse began when Blewie was given out lbw to a Srinath off-cutter that was moving so far down leg side it should have been called a wide. To make matters worse, Umpire K Parthasaradhi was in no position for an lbw call as he was halfway between the stumps and mid-on when he raised his pudgy little black finger. I had a better view back in the rooms and I was half way between the fridge and the dunny! Anyway, Tubs went soon after for 45, followed by Ponts (9) and Junior (0). By this stage we were looking like a defeated team, with each batsman walking out like a man on his way to the gallows. This, in my opinion, is a big mistake. Cricket is such a mind game and the opposition can sense apprehension and fear merely in a batsman's body language. That's why when I'm going out to bat I like to swagger a little, look round, casually spit and break wind. Then, when I'm out of the dressing room, I stride purposefully out to the pitch and eyeball my opponents. Unfortunately, though, all the body language in the world couldn't save me today as I became another victim of the Srinath/Parthasaradhi lbw combination. Like Blewie, I was stunned by the decision and, understandably, muttered a few quiet words under my breath as I departed the pitch. And I do mean 'quiet' — anyone more than 100 metres away would have struggled to hear what I said.

No one else put up any serious resistance and soon after tea we were all out for 181. No one felt much like celebrating after the match but Tubs made his usual insistence that at least a few representatives

Understandably, I muttered a few quiet words under my breath.

from the Australian team join the Indians in their room for a congratulatory drink. After a brief discussion it was agreed that we'd send our scorer Mike Walsh and two blokes who are over here on a supporters' tour. The rest of us returned to the hotel.

Now, I'm a big believer that no matter how bad a defeat is, you can always find something positive in it. Today, for example, our early collapse meant we got back to the Taj Bengal in time for happy hour. And we've got tomorrow off. In fact, that's two positives.

After a few media commitments and dinner we all spent the evening at the hotel bar watching the Ansett Cup Grand Final on cable. After this, a couple of us decided to grab a cab and visit a few nightspots. We ended up at some joint called the Equinox which is rated as one of the classiest clubs in Calcutta (meaning it's got an indoor dunny), where Ponts got into a scuffle with some local chick. It was all a bit of harmless fun, just a few pushes and shoves, hardly a punch thrown, when all of a sudden security arrived and chucked us all out. It all

It's good sportsmanship to acknowledge the other team's victory.

happened so quickly some of us barely had time to put our pants back on. I was practically thrown down the stairs by some bouncer who then had the nerve to call out, 'Any chance of an autograph?' We eventually found a cab and returned home at the end of a pretty miserable day and one we hopefully won't have to think about again.

Ponting in Nightclub Brawl!
Disco Duck Ponting

● BY YUSAALI RAJANESHI

AUSTRALIAN batsman Ricky Ponting was involved in an ugly nightclub incident last night after allegedly insulting a female journalist. The controversy comes just a few hours after it was revealed that fellow Australian batsman, the recently recalled Warwick Todd, will be facing disciplinary action after a verbal run-in yesterday with Indian umpire K Parthasaradhi. According to Mr Parthasaradhi's match report, 'He (Todd) denied being out lbw, calling me a "dirty cheating curry-muncher", and accused me of stealing the Australian team's roulette wheel.' Neither Ponting nor Todd were available for comment. *(CONTINUED Page 77)*

Day 31 ✌ (Sun Mar 22)

Today was supposed to be a rest day but team management felt it was best to leave Calcutta a.s.a.p. Consequently we had the unpleasant task of packing, checking out and travelling to the airport, all at a hideously early hour of the morning.

Honestly, the standard of journalism over here is the pits. According to one report of last night's incident there was a 'brawl', sparked by Ponts who was 'found making obscene gestures to a woman'. Now my memory of the evening is a little hazy (that Kingfisher beer is lethal stuff) but I know for a fact Ponts was doing nothing more than mucking around, pulling his zipper up and down for the benefit of a few local chicks. 'Obscene'? That very routine is part of at least a dozen sportsmen's nights' routines. As for the 'woman' who complained, she was Indian and a journalist (so an unreliable witness on two counts) and obviously had no idea what she was talking about. Take this quote for example: 'It's not the sort of thing you expect from an Australian cricketer.' Shows how little she knows.

But as usual team management were not interested in hearing our side of the story and upon arrival in Bangalore, Ponts was summoned to a hearing with Steve Bernard, tour director Cam Battersby and Tubs. Steve and Cam were both furious with Ponts; Tubs just felt he should get back to basics. After their meeting a press statement was released in which it was revealed that a 'substantial' fine had been imposed, believed to be four figures. (What we kept quiet was the fact these figures were in rupees.) In addition, Ponts was required to release a formal written apology, the first draft of which apparently read, 'Sorry for flashing me old fella at the Hindu chick.' Team management later refined it a little and Ponts ended up saying that he 'unreservedly apologised'. At the end of the day, the great pity is that this sort of controversial nightclub incident will not help Ponting's dream of one day becoming Australian captain. Although he has been sounded out about joining the Channel 9 commentary team.

On the subject of captaincy, it's funny how one or two black marks against your name can really hurt a player's leadership ambitions. Back in '94 when AB was looking set to retire as skipper there were a few obvious contenders for his replacement: Tubs, Heals, Tugga and myself. The four of us got together and agreed that whoever received the nod would have the full support of the other three. Naturally we were all lying. As it turned out of course Tubs won the job and a year or two later I found out why I was overlooked. Apparently the powers that be weren't too happy with a small incident back in 1992 when I drank 48 cans of Foster's during a team flight. Now I know what you're thinking — other players like Boonie and Rod Marsh have done far worse — but, as it was explained to me, their record-breaking stints were on board Sydney to London flights. My 48 cans were consumed between Sydney and Melbourne. Still, it's a fine line.

On the home front, there's been a hitch with the renovations. Turns out our neighbours, the Trans, have objected to the council over our

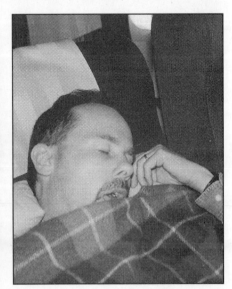

Forty-eight reasons why I never made captain.

building plans. Honestly, those people have been trouble from the day they moved in. None of them speaks a word of English (except the son, who's apparently a lawyer and filed the objection) and there must be thirty of them living in the one house. Not that we've ever said anything, even when they ripped down a perfectly good pergola and planted a bloody vegetable garden. Anyway, exterior work on the extensions has pretty much ground to a halt but Ros assured me that while the planning appeal is heard Barry's got plenty to keep him busy inside.

Day 32 ✌ (Mon 23 Mar)

Bangalore is known as the 'Garden City' and, if the amount of mould growing in my bathroom is any indication, it's obviously a fertile place. Another hideously early wake-up call had us assembling at 11.00 for the customary team tour photo. A suitable location was found and, as with all official photographs, the captain sat in the middle, flanked by coach, manager and vice-captain. After this the seating arrangements got a little complicated. Heals felt the front row should be occupied by players with the most number of Tests under their belt. Junior thought we should also take the one-dayers into account. Someone else believed it should be based on age. I suggested total match fines was the measure, it was rapidly developing into a total rabble. Just when we finally got things sorted out, a few of the lads announced they wanted their managers and personal sponsors in the shot, which was totally ridiculous as there weren't nearly enough chairs. In the end the whole thing turned into a complete bunfight and I think the team photo suffered as a result.

After everyone had calmed down a special team meeting was called for 6.00 this evening. With the third Test just a few days away Tubs and Swampy invited everyone in the squad to suggest reasons why we are yet to win a big match. In my experience this sort of 'open forum' meeting can often be dangerous, with

The Australian squad in India, 1998.

batsmen and bowlers basically just turning on each other, but today's was very positive. Possibly because the bowlers weren't invited. We all agreed that the heat was a major factor. It's incredible the amount of fluid a player loses over the course of a hot day. I remember years ago the ACB conducted some tests on this very phenomenon. We were up in Brisbane for a practice match and when we arrived at the rooms prior to a tour match we were all told to strip. 'Shit,' I thought, 'not another one of Simmo's team bonding sessions.' But it was a test to determine fluid loss. Each of us was weighed nude before we batted and then again after we'd been dismissed, but before enjoying a post-innings drink. The results were startling. We learnt that the average player loses 3.5 kilos during a one-hour innings. We also learnt that Merv Hughes should never remove his clothes in public. The difficulty of playing in high temperatures is not only the physical strain but also the fact that after a day in the sun all of us are having to drink litres of water each night to prevent cramping. Then of course you find yourself constantly getting up and going to the loo, which can be a real pain because they can be pretty crowded at a lot of nightclubs.

Another major concern is the food. Without wanting to sound like Warney, there's only so much rice, boiled chicken and naan a person can eat. And finally, there's the obvious battle with injuries. So far we've had Tubs, Tugga, Blocker and Pistol all missing games through injury or illness. Even today another two players joined the casualty list. Adam Dale succumbed to a gastric complaint (much to the mirth of all the lads) while our new arrival Flem has lived up to his nickname by developing a respiratory problem.

An interesting bit of news from abroad today — Mike Atherton has stood down as captain of England after yet another personal and team failure. There was an article on his resignation in the paper this morning in which Atherton spoke about no longer feeling he had the respect or confidence of his players. I found his thoughts so interesting I cut the article out and shoved it under Tubs' door.

Day 33 ✌ (Tues 24 Mar)

On the eve of the third Test tomorrow it was disappointing to discover that yet again the Australian press had turned on us. A variety of newspaper articles appeared this morning with journos questioning everything from our fitness to our commitment. As a player you can ignore critical comments from sportswriters like Robert Craddock and Malcolm Knox; they're just frustrated journos having to fill column space by bagging blokes having an honest go. But critical comments from the likes of David Hookes or Keith Stackpole really hurt, because they once shared the same baggy green cap and should therefore know better. I remember during my form slump during the '97 England Ashes tour former Australian captain Ian Chappell had some very strong words to say about me. He called me 'stupid', 'gutless' and a 'hopeless failure'. Fortunately these words never appeared in print — they were yelled at me in a pub in Leeds. But they still hurt.

After breakfast we travelled down to the ground for a final practice session before tomorrow's game. Flem was too sick to make it but Adam 'Chip'n' Dale crawled out of his sickbed for the all-important net session. Another eager member of the squad was Darren 'Boof' Lehmann, who was told today he will be replacing the injured Tugga. It's a much-deserved reward for the young South Australian who has notched up over 8000 first class runs. Within minutes of hearing the news he was on the phone, speaking to his family and putting together a book deal. Perhaps the unluckiest member of our squad, leg-spinner Stuart McGill, was told at training that he will again be missing out on a game. There's no doubt one of the toughest jobs in the world is touring with a cricket team yet never getting picked to play and it's a credit to Magilla that, when told the news, it only took half an hour to talk him down off the roof.

At the team meeting before a Test we like to go through each member of the opposition and identify his weaknesses but this wasn't so easy. The best we could come up with was:

Sidhu: he's short

Laxman: bats with a short partner

Dravid: once made a duck on a youth tour of the West Indies

Tendulkar: often loses concentration approaching a double century

Azharuddin: doesn't drink.

After that we sort of gave up on their weaknesses and decided to look at our own strategy. One of the problems we've been facing in the field is that a lot of the Indian team don't speak English and are therefore very difficult to unsettle verbally. That's when I played my trump card, producing a little booklet I'd picked up in Calcutta that listed a dozen offensive Hindi and Tamil expressions. Little gems like:

Poondah — poofta

Dai soothala pootan — stick it up your bum.

Dai teh vedia mahana — son of a prostitute.

Plus a whole lot more that could be used to question everything from a player's sexuality and physical endowment through to the authenticity of his hair. We all spent a few minutes learning a selection of these phrases and left the meeting feeling pumped up and confident. Even Junior, and he can be a real poondah when it comes to this sort of stuff.

Sharjah is officially alcohol free so we brought a few provisions.

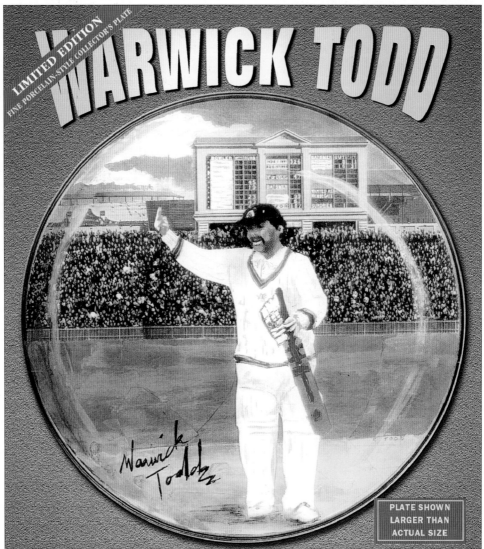

LIMITED EDITION
FINE PORCELAIN-STYLE COLLECTOR'S PLATE

WARWICK TODD

PLATE SHOWN
LARGER THAN
ACTUAL SIZE

Share One of Warwick Todd's Greatest Moments
Sydney Cricket Ground, 1989 – Australia vs. England

As the sun set late in the afternoon Warwick Todd stepped towards the square leg umpire and gave him the bird, before storming off the field to huge applause and a meeting with the match referee. What made this moment even more unique was that Warwick hadn't been selected to play that day—he was just driving past the ground and wanted to make a statement about declining umpiring standards. Now you can own a piece of cricket history, authentically captured by award-winning sporting artist Roslyn Todd.

Yours for just 20 easy payments of $50

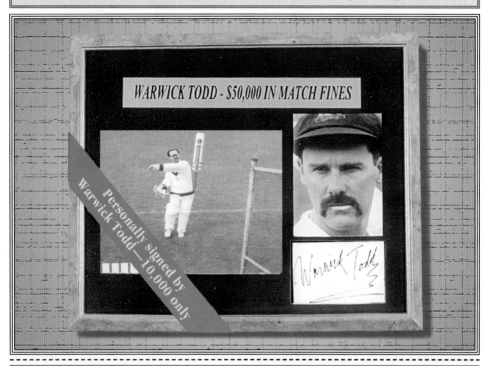

Warwick Todd

There's not a lot to do in India and watching pitch preparations rates as a pretty big day out. (That's the Indian Board of Selectors on our left.)

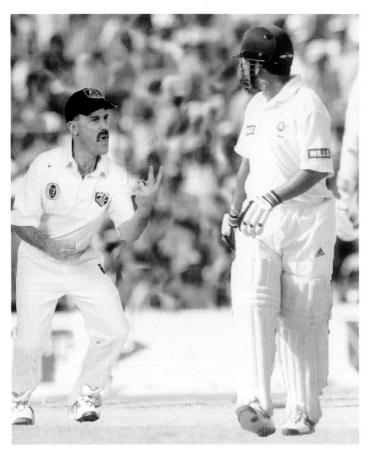

The much anticipated Warne vs Tendulkar battle was nothing compared to the Todd vs Tendulkar clash. Here I show the cocky little curry-muncher the way to the dressing room. Both of them.

Day 34 ✌ (Wed 25 Mar)

3rd Test
India vs Australia, Day 1

The first morning of a Test is always an exciting one and my pre-match routine remains pretty much the same. To ensure peak fitness I practice a technique known as gyrotonics which combines breathing exercises with an extensive series of body stretches and muscle warm-ups. It can be pretty exhausting but the good thing is the whole routine can be completed without getting out of bed. As can breakfast.

There were two players making their Test debut today — Boof Lehmann and Chip'n Dale — and you could tell they were both a little nervous, sitting up the front of the bus in full team gear. One of them had even shaved!

Arriving at the M Chinnaswamy Stadium we went about the usual tasks of sorting out gear and claiming the best seats in the dressing room, either under a fan, near the fridge or as far away from Swampy as possible. Unfortunately, Tubs lost the toss and not surprisingly the home team elected to bat. But for the first time in the series we made an early breakthrough: Laxman caught Tubby bowled Kaspa for just 6. Even though no more wickets fell before lunch our bowlers managed to stem the run flow by keeping the ball up, outside off and away from Robbo (28 off his first two overs!). At one stage Sidhu started to look dangerous and so Tubs moved me in close where I was able to offer a few bilingual pleasantries. Just as Warney came into bowl I muttered 'Dai soothala poondah', which in hindsight I realised meant 'Hey, you've got no bum'. Whether the Indian opener was insulted or simply confused I'll never know, but he played the next ball on and departed for 74. At 3 for 110 the home side looked a little shaky but then that

He may be destitute, but at least he's fitter than any Australian bowler.

man Tendulkar arrived and proceeded to knock up yet another century.

It was a long, hot day in the field and a few ice-cold beers certainly went down well in the rooms this afternoon as we toasted Boof and Chip'n on making their Test debuts. Tubs even said a few words, something along the lines of 'Put that f*#king beer away we've still got a session to play', which kind of put a dampener on things. After the tea interval Tendulkar continued his run feast and by stumps the Indians were looking good at 4 for 290. Not looking good was Warney, or, more particularly, his groin. The big blond leggie suffered a severe strain during play and may be doubtful to take any further part in the match. On an even more serious note, he may be forced to sit out tonight's Dirty Dancing competition.

Day 35 ✌ (Thur 26 Mar)

3rd Test
India vs Australia, Day 2

I was woken this morning by the noise from our hotel's air-conditioning unit, a fearsome din so loud it sounded as if I were sleeping on top of the bloody thing. Turned out I was. How I managed to pass out on the Taj's rooftop remains a mystery but I suspect our sponsor's product may yet again have been involved.

With the possibility that we may end up batting today I was keen to have a practice session and so I got a few of the

I was woken this morning by the noise from our hotel's air-conditioning unit.

younger bowlers to toss me a few balls before the game started. Of course, it's not possible to play a full range of shots on the team bus but at least it got my feet moving. Down at the ground things got off to a good start with Chip'n taking his first ever Test wicket: Ganguly lbw for 17. I don't know which was the bigger surprise, Dale getting someone out or an Indian umpire upholding an lbw appeal. Tendulkar followed soon after but not before he'd notched up a massive 177. Of course, Tendulkar's success in this series is due to more than just natural talent, there was a hell of a lot of hard work involved. Before the series even began he apparently arranged for as many spinners as he could find to bowl into roughed-up turf outside his leg stump. The obvious lesson is that nothing improves a player like sheer, solid practice and with this in mind I decided to try the same thing. Last Monday I arranged for McGill, Robbo and Dale to bowl for an hour and a half in the nets and sure enough, it did them all a lot of good. Next week I might even join them.

We eventually dismissed the home team for 424 and it was our turn to bat. Slats got the innings off to a flying start with an aggressive 91. Unfortunately Tubs went cheaply again, departing the crease with just 14 against his name. A third quick wicket saw the Aussie dressing room in a state of semi-panic. Middle-order batsmen — who a few moments earlier had been relaxing over a game of cards — searching frantically for their creams, Junior rushing off to find his bookmaker, Swampy on the phone desperately trying to cancel the three kegs he'd ordered for the post-match celebrations. Outside, the home crowd was sensing an Aussie collapse, blowing trumpets and setting fire to news-papers. Some spectators even managed to bring firecrackers into the ground and play was often interrupted by mini explosions and puffs of smoke. (Imagine if this country ever gets its hands on a nuclear weapon!) At stumps we managed to reach 3 for 209, still 115 runs in arrears. Ahead of us lay a lot of hard work. Not to mention a sponsor's function and drinks at the hotel to welcome our one-day contingent arriving tonight.

Day 36 ✌ (Fri Mar 27)

3rd Test
India vs Australia, Day 3

More injury worries for the team this morning with Junior vomiting uncontrollably. The official media line was 'viral infection' but just quietly the words 'Southern Comfort' may have been a little closer to the truth. Fortunately Hooter was able to give the plucky New South Welshman an injection that got him onto the field where he went about compiling a swashbuckling 153 not out. It was Junior's four-teenth Test century and confirmed his place as one of the world's best batsmen. The only real criticism you could make about the younger Waugh twin is his 'casual' style. Whenever Junior gets out he simply shrugs his shoulders, curses inwardly and walks off. As an Australian batsman I think you're obliged to do more than this and that's why whenever I'm dismissed I always make a point of either cursing loudly, knocking over the stumps, glaring at the umpire or tossing my bat. Sometimes all at once. Frankly, I think you owe it to the kids watching. That said, expressing disappointment at getting out can sometimes land you in hot water. A match against South Africa at the SCG last year springs to mind. I was given out in pretty dubious circumstances and, as I was heading off the field, I kicked one of the South African's helmets about 10 metres through the air. Result: a $10 000 match fine. And I was forced to apologise to Adam Bacher, who was wearing the helmet at the time. So you've gotta take care.

Sadly Junior was the only Aussie to get among the runs and by the time I came in the score was delicately poised at 4 for 312. The Indians were looking confident, obviously sensing an Australian collapse so I made sure I took plenty of time walking to the wicket, taking guard,

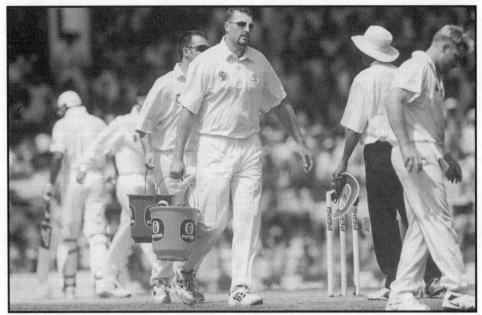

With half the team suffering gastro it wasn't always possible to make it off the field in time. Who'd wanna be 12th man today?

looking round. This sort of delaying tactic can really frustrate a bowler and break his rhythm. Mind games are such an important part of modern cricket and I like to make the opposition wait, dictate the pace, let them know who's in command. This is a technique I employ whenever I'm on a cricket field, even if it sometimes gets me in trouble — as it did at Lord's in '93. Once again we were under pressure, it was a big occasion and I refused to be rushed. I strolled out into the middle, looked around, scratched my nuts, spat, fiddled with my protector. Only then, when I was completely ready did I shake the Queen's hand.

Unfortunately my delaying tactics failed to work today and I was out to Kumble for just 16. By the end of the day we were all out for 400, a deficit of 24 runs. Looking back on today's play what really upsets me is the easy way we collapsed. When the wickets started to fall no one was prepared to put in the hard yards, to put their hand up and say, 'I'm going to stop this, I'm going to lift us out of trouble.' Heals did put his hand up, but that was only to ask if the Star TV cocktail party was still on for tonight. It is.

Day 37 ✌ (Sat 28 Mar)

3rd Test
India vs Australia, Day 4

Well, it's been a long time coming but today we finally won a Test match in India, the first Aussie team to do so since Bill Lawry was here in '69. Somehow it was destined to be a great day. The Indians started their second innings slowly, losing 3 wickets for 99. But with Tendulkar and Azharuddin still at the crease anything was possible. That's when Kaspa stepped in with a magnificent spell of bowling to take 5/12. For the first time on tour I actually felt the Indian batsmen were under real pressure. Tubs moved the field up, Kaspa was steaming in, 'Have a go you poofters' the situation seemed to be saying. Actually, it wasn't the situation, it was me.

By the first over after lunch we'd knocked over an excellent chicken tikka and the home team for just 169, a lead of only 193. Of course, Australian teams have been notoriously bad at chasing small totals, a fact not lost on Junior and Ponts who both put $500 on us to lose. But during the break Tubs spoke about the need to keep focused and not 'count our chickens before they've hatched'. It was a little hard to hear everything he said as we were already three verses into our victory song but I think that was the general gist. For once both Tubs and Slats got a good start, and we had little trouble picking off the required runs for the loss of just one wicket. I tell you, the celebrations in our rooms after the match were something special. 'Under the Southern Cross' was sung again and again with such gusto and pride I was immediately covered in goosebumps. Not to mention beer, champagne, bourbon and something Robbo was drinking from a two litre flagon.

Kaspa was named Man of the Match and rightly so — his five wickets

Tubs did well not to let the press upset him.

in pretty tough conditions helped win the game for us. To see the big Queenslander down on his knees struggling to breathe made you realise what a huge effort he'd put in. And this was during post-match celebrations. You should have seen him out on the field.

Especially pleasing about today's historic victory was the fact I managed to souvenir a stump, not always easy after an exciting Test win. Fortunately Slats wasn't looking and I managed to lift one out of his bag. It will now be added to my private cricket museum back home. I'm very proud of my memorabilia collection and believe it performs an important function, educating people about the history of this great game. I'm always pleased to see the look of delight on a young kid's face as I show them round my display and I firmly believe the modest entrance fee is more than justified.

Naturally there were quite a few press commitments after the match and, disappointingly, some of the local media focused unnecessarily on the fact that it was a 'dead rubber'. This line of questioning detracted from the great effort we'd all put in over the past four days and Tubs did well not to let it upset him. I wasn't quite so restrained. I guess I've still got a few lessons to learn in the area of media relations.

I guess I've still got a few lessons to learn in the area of media relations.

Day 38 ✌ (Sun March 29)

Coming home from a big night on the town.

Well, our injury toll continues to grow, with Heals now sporting a nasty gash above his left eyebrow. He foolishly stood on a table last night to sing the team song and was hit by a ceiling fan. Word is management may consider making helmets compulsory for future renditions.

But nothing could dampen our spirits after a great victory and we certainly enjoyed the celebrations last night. The last thing I remember was jumping onto a camel round dawn and heading through the streets of Bangalore. On the way I bumped into Slats and Boof who hopped up too and together we lumbered into the lobby of the Taj West End Hotel. They're apparently still trying to clean the carpet from where a small 'accident' took place. (I told Slats he shouldn't mix his drinks.)

Our celebrations were cut short by Tubs, however, who dropped this bombshell in the press today:

Taylor hints at quitting Test captaincy

Our skipper has made no secret of the fact he dislikes the Australian Cricket Board's two-captain policy and its destabilising effect. If Tubs does resign as Test captain I guess Tugga will take over as there aren't too many other candidates. Heals is a bit of a loose cannon, Junior's a bit 'laid back' for leadership and Ponts' position as

I'll Be Captain — Todd

■ BY JONATHAN FELDERS (CRICKET CORRESPONDENT)

INDIA: Australian batsman Warwick Todd has offered his services as captain of the Test team should current skipper Mark Taylor stand down. Asked if he'd be prepared to lead the team, a typically modest Todd replied, 'Shit yeah. Should have been doing it for years.'

head of the social committee is too important to risk jeopardising. Then of course there's yours truly. Not that being Australian captain is something I think about much. Often hours go by without the thought popping into my head. Obviously it would be a huge honour, not to mention a guaranteed path to the Channel 9 commentary team, but I'm hardly about to go round suggesting it.

I personally have no problems with the current two-team policy, provided of course I'm part of both. My only reservation would be the fact that a lot of the one-day players are young blokes who come into the Aussie side without any real respect for us senior players or the traditions of the game. They sit anywhere they like in dressing rooms, expect to speak at team meetings, demand gym facilities at all hotels. I remember when I first joined the Australian team no one spoke to me for three years. And rightly so — as a young bloke I had to earn their respect. Give you a typical example of how younger, one-day 'specialists' often fail to appreciate the traditions of this great game. When asked to sign a team bat they'll often rush in and put their name at the top, whereas I was taught you always leave the most prominent spot for the captain and senior players. A correctly autographed bat should look something like this:

Day 39 ✌ (Mon March 30)

In an effort to maintain peak physical fitness, Hooter organised a gym session this morning for 9.00 am sharp. The team was divided into two groups: those who showed up and the rest of us.

After Hooter's gym session sort of petered out (it's never much fun on your own), sightseeing was on the agenda with the Bangalore tourism office organising a trip to some local Hindu temples and monuments. One place we stopped at was called the Bull Temple and it's considered so holy that visitors are expected to remove their shoes at the door, bow slightly and leave a small donation. Interestingly, those are the exact same instructions that apply when visiting Mark Taylor's hotel room.

Speaking of Tubs, our skipper left for home today. It was sad watching him get in a cab and wave goodbye on his way to the airport but deep down we all knew we'd be seeing him again soon. We'd pinched his passport and hidden it back at the hotel.

With no match tomorrow the afternoon was declared 'free time' and I decided to do a little sightseeing of my own. Renting a car and driving yourself is considered not advisable here in India. I soon discovered why.

On the positive side, there's plenty of public transport available and I found most drivers more than willing to help if you offer the right tip.

Driving yourself is considered not advisable here in India. I soon discovered why.

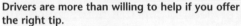
Drivers are more than willing to help if you offer the right tip.

Back at the hotel I was disappointed to learn that the ACB had decided to fine me $2000 over an incident that took place on day three of the Third Test. It involved a rather heated exchange between myself and the diminutive spinner Kumble outside the Indian dressing rooms. Now I'll admit I was at fault, I started the argument, I pushed over the chair, I threw the first bottle. But, and this is what really gets my goat, why does the ACB need to step in now when the matter had been adequately dealt with? That very night I was forced to appear before team management who had no hesitation in handing out a severe punishment. I was banned from Sunday's team trivia night and will have to sit up the back of the bus for the next two weeks. But still the ACB refuse to accept that team discipline should be kept in-house.

If Steve Waugh doesn't put that bloody camera away I'll shove it up his arse. (Photo: Steve Waugh)

Day 40 ✌ (Tues March 31)

Feeling good today. Twenty-four hours away from the first one-day international and we've had a training session, a team meeting and a darned good curry. All at the same time. The only negative to come out of the day was an article that appeared in the Adelaide *Advertiser* in which some 'journalist' rated my form so far on tour as 'average'. It's lucky I take no interest in what the press say about me and I probably would not even have seen the article had the media monitoring agency I employ not faxed it to me. I will be honest and admit my batting is not back to its very best and it's a little difficult to know what I should do. I remember a similar slump I went through back in the late 1980s. I spoke to our then-coach Bob Simpson, who organised some extra net sessions. We spent hours together every day going over my technique, analysing my strengths and weaknesses. Eventually I cottoned on to what was wrong — I was spending too much time with Simmo. What I now realise (and didn't back then) is that cricket is above all a mental game. That's why I rarely bother to train. But I think about training, a lot.

Today was a travel day, with the boys flying from Bangalore to the pleasant coastal town of Cochin in the state of Kerala. As always our plane was delayed, meaning many hours of sitting round an airport departure lounge. Such constant stuff-ups with transport could easily unsettle a side but I'm pleased to say the boys handled the long delay with patience and maturity. Team spirit is so good that on the bus to the hotel we even held another farting competition.

An interesting fact from the guidebook: Kerala is India's most literate state, with over 70 per cent of the population capable of both reading and writing. Which is 5 per cent more than you'll find within the current Australian squad. Unfortunately the people of Cochin decided to give us an official 'cultural welcome' featuring some local dance troupe. It was this bloody ballet thing called Kathakali that dates back four or five hundred years, which was roughly how long the performance took. Now I'm no dance critic (although Ros and I have done a little boot-scootin' in our time), but this was an absolute shocker. I mean, there's only so long you can watch six Hindu chicks with finger cymbals wave a bit of incense round. Needless to say, it was a bloody long night and we all envied the newly arrived Bevo who escaped the performance after coming down with food poisoning (much to the amusement of the lads). At least he's getting among the runs!*

Typical press photo, focusing on the one time I wasn't paying attention. Mind you, it was bloody boring.

---

*This joke is part of my highly successful sportsmen's night routine and is therefore copyright.

Day 41 ✌ (Wed April 1)

One-day International
Australia vs India

Eighty thousand fans packed the J Nehru Stadium this morning, many camping outside to get tickets. You've gotta admire the dedication of Indian cricket supporters, it's not exactly pleasant spending a night sleeping on the streets. As I discovered myself last night. That Kingfisher beer should really carry a health warning.

Inside the ground it was like a sauna, and Swampy — who played in the famous Madras tied Test — declared today was even hotter. Not that he ever moved more than five feet from the dressing room fan. To make matters worse Hindi music blared from loudspeakers all round the ground. It was that bad we could barely hear 'Khe Sahn' in our

That Kingfisher beer should really carry a health warning.

91

rooms. And the home team even had their own cheer squad. I kid you not, a bunch of Indian women were leading the crowd, though naturally they were all modestly clad in the traditional female dress of India, the sari. (The traditional male dress is of course the brown polyester shirt.)

India won the toss and batted first, but it was Kaspa who led the way with two wicket maidens. The big Queenslander went on to take three wickets but conditions obviously made it tough. By the end of his ten overs Kaspa was clearly distressed, down on his haunches gasping for air. I haven't seen a cricketer so totally knackered since Arjuna Ranatunga ran three at the SCG (And he was using a runner at the time.) Despite Kaspa's efforts the home team managed to score 5 for 309, their highest ever one day total against Australia. On a disappointing note, the newly arrived Tom Moody was pelted in the outfield by all sorts of objects. Naturally Tugga complained to the umpires but they were powerless to stop this sort of behaviour from a section of the crowd who were obviously drunk and ignorant. As it turned out, the projectiles were coming largely from a group of Australians over here on a supporters' tour.

We knew we needed a good start and our openers Gilly (61) and Junior (28) gave us just that. But as so often happens a few quick wickets saw the Aussie innings stall. I tell you, there's nothing worse than having a quiet smoke on the dunny and hearing a roar from outside. Then another. You hope desperately it's just Junior and

Ready for battle.

92

Ponts listening to some race meeting but no — wickets are falling. Time to zip up, butt out the fag and face the music.

I came in at the 27th over with the score at 106. Tendulkar of all people was bowling and the home-team hero had already taken a few wickets so I really knew a big innings was needed. I have a mantra I repeat to myself at the crease: 'Concentrate, watch the ball, concentrate.' I was in the middle of mouthing these very words when suddenly I thought of something — I may have forgotten to flush the toilet. Next thing I know I'm adjudged to be out lbw by umpire SK Bansal, who obviously takes a pretty liberal view of what constitutes 'leg before wicket'. Anything bowled by an Indian would seem to qualify. Sadly we were all out for just 268, giving the home side victory by 41 runs.

After the match Tugga hit out at the lack of crowd control. Several of us were almost hit by cement thrown from upper stands and once again some bottles landed within metres of Moody. Our manager Brute Bernard said he would lodge an official complaint with the president of the Board of Control for Cricket, Mr Raj Singh Dungarpur. I even offered to chuck it through his window.

Day 42 ✌ (Thurs April 2)

Cricket's a funny game. One moment you've won a Test and are on top of the world, the next you've lost a match and facing the critics. I was thinking about this very phenomenon over a few beers late last night when the next thing I knew it was time for breakfast. Come to think of it, it was very late. After my usual morning meal (toast and six Beroccas) it was off to the airport for yet another flight, this time to Ahmedabad, the capital of Guratji. We received a rather unpleasant shock as we touched down when the pilot calmly declared, 'Welcome to Ahmedabad, where the current ground temperature is 40 degrees.' At first I thought it was just Ponts making another of his bogus in-flight announcements (earlier in the flight the madcap Taswegian had informed passengers the cockpit was on fire and burning out of control!) but upon leaving the plane we realised it really was that hot. If the extreme heat wasn't enough to contend with there were even more stomach problems for the team today. Ponts and Marto had gastro (much to the mirth of all the lads) while yours truly strained an abdominal muscle attempting an early morning sit-up. When will I ever learn? Of course, the threat of gastro is a constant one and as touring cricketers we all understand the importance of watching what we eat. I've known nine members of a sixteen man squad to all be in bed with stomach bugs just from drinking the local water. And this was in Adelaide.

Disappointing news greeted me at the hotel. Apparently I've been reported to the match referee following yesterday's game in which I allegedly 'verbally abused' umpire SK Bansal. Honestly, what's the game coming to if a player can't, in the heat of the moment, express mild disappointment with a decision? Yes, I did say a few words to Bansal but what's the problem with that? Okay, the exchange did take

Tonight's meeting was the best of the tour so far.

place outside his hotel room at about 3.00 am but I was still wound up. And why get the match referee involved? I guess there'll be another fine coming my way, which is the standard disciplinary measure we players face. As a cricketer you can be warned, fined, suspended or — the ultimate international sanction — have Ian Chappell turn on you.

Tonight's meeting was, I believe, the best of the tour so far. It was cancelled.

Day 43 ✌ (Fri April 3)

One-day International
Australia vs Zimbabwe

When you're playing a team like Zimbabwe who aren't exactly world-beaters, the biggest problem you can face is complacency. Tugga spoke about this at length this morning, just before announcing that the pre-match warm-up had been cancelled.

Security remains a concern after our last match but at least the ground here at the Sardar Patel Stadium is surrounded by a moat filled with broken glass. The water in the moat is pretty murky and you can't actually see the glass but we know it's there because we chucked over 200 stubbies in after celebrating a '96 World Cup semi-final win. Not that a moat is going to stop crowds throwing objects onto the field. As Tugga said to the press after the match on Wednesday, 'If something's not done a top player could easily have a sparkling career destroyed.' He was of course referring to Tom Moody and therefore stretching the truth a little, but the point remains a good one.

Faced with another day of 40 degree temperatures Kaspa was forced to pull out with exhaustion. The big Queenslander simply couldn't face another day in the field and we all assured him he shouldn't feel he was letting the team down.*

We won the toss and elected to bat, with our opener Gilly falling early to one of the all-time worst lbw decisions ever seen on the sub-continent. The big fella was absolutely ropable when he got back into our rooms and it took him quite some time to stop swearing and calm down. (From memory it was round June.) A few more quick wickets saw

----

*Though of course, he was.

me join Ponts for what needed to be a lengthy partnership. In situations like this communication between batsmen is vital. I'll always go out of my way to speak with a partner, let him know how he's playing and where he's looking vulnerable. Funnily enough, the compliment is not often returned. For example, today I pointed out to Ponts how he was shuffling dangerously across his stumps. But I got nothing in the way of help back from him. Admittedly he was out next ball shuffling across his stumps but you still think he might have said something. As it turned out, I also fell cheaply, slashing at a wide delivery for just 8. Another failure and I can feel the pressure mounting.

We were eventually dismissed for 252 and the Zimbabwe boys began their innings, racing to 1 for 143 in the first 30 overs. Things weren't helped when Tugga dropped Murray Goodwin on 18 (he went on to make 55) but thanks to some good work in the field by those whose minds weren't preoccupied with gaining the Test captaincy we managed to dismiss the opposition in the final over for 239. Our 13 run victory was soured by yet further crowd misbehaviour, with Tom Moody again pelted by rocks and bottles. According to the ground authorities, an extra 750 security men had been hired for today's game but the problem was they were doing most of the throwing. Honestly, security in this part of the world is a joke, and it's not just on field that problems are occurring. This afternoon I was enjoying a quiet beer after the game when I looked up to find someone standing over me in the dressing room yelling, 'You're an idiot! You're an idiot!' Turned out it was just Hooksey conducting an interview for Foxtel, but I really feel he should have been stopped at the door.

Postscript. It's now the early hours of Saturday morning and I'm sitting in my room staring at this diary. The words read 'Another failure, time to quit.' I try to convince myself I'm just tired and depressed but I can't help thinking, 'Maybe those simple words are true, maybe it is "time to quit"'. Then I realise something. It's not my handwriting. When I find out who's been writing in my diary I'll bloody kill them.

Day 44 ✌ (Sat April 4)

While India were busy defeating Zimbabwe today in Baroda we were once again in the air en route to Kanpur. After checking into the hotel I managed to catch up with my old mate Dave Corcorran, who's working over here for some computer company. Dave and I used to go to school together and it was great meeting up for a beer and a chat. Old friendships are something I treasure and over the years no matter how 'big' I've got in the world of international cricket I never forget the blokes I've done better than. Schoolmates, district cricket players, family friends — we may not see much of each other but every Christmas you can be guaranteed they'll all receive something in the mail from W Todd. And if they like my new book they've got 60 days to pay or return it and owe nothing.*

*Except of course postage.

Posing with fans can be a pain but when one of them's got a gun, who's gonna say no? Not that Warney ever says no to a camera.

After lunch we had a rare opportunity to play a round of golf at a fairly mediocre local course. Yet again our lives were made miserable by the hordes of autograph seekers. What happens is you sign one and suddenly a crowd forms, with eager fans jostling and pushing. It's like being in a nightclub with Ponts. As well as autograph hunters we were beseiged by locals wanting a photo. It's not easy to say no, especially when many of them are armed. In the end all you can do is grin and bear it.

Taking in some traditional Indian dancing.

After dinner a few of the lads went out to enjoy a bit of local culture, taking in a traditional Indian dance performance. Well, I guess it wasn't strictly 'traditional', as the performance took place largely on a table, but the woman involved was wearing a sari. At first.

Day 45 ✌ (Sun April 5)

There's nothing worse than being woken up early on one of your few days off but this is exactly what happened to me this morning. The garbos round this hotel are so bloody noisy and at 7.30 my sleep was shattered by an almighty crash, followed by an extremely loud truck emptying a dump-master. It sounded like I was asleep in the actual bin which, it turned out, I was.

Most of last night remains a blur. I remember staggering out of the club with a few of the lads and taking a taxi. And then the taxidriver running after us demanding we bring it back. And after that it's all a blank. Must have been a top night.

Anyway, I managed to crawl out of the bin before any real damage was done and made it inside for breakfast where there was some pretty

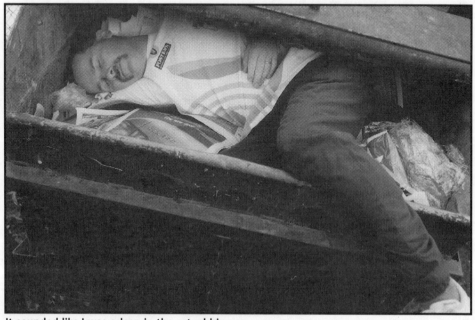

It sounded like I was asleep in the actual bin.

bad news. An all-day training session called by Swampy. According to our coach we were 'coasting' and needed to show more effort, more determination. He gave us a real blast and his words must have hit home because the intensity at training this morning was clearly much improved. So much so we agreed to call the session off early and hit the pub. Keeping your fluids up is vital over here.

On the way back to our hotel I was once again struck by the number of children playing cricket. Every park, vacant field and street seemed to have its own 'mini-Test' under way. When you see the enthusiasm of these kids it's little wonder India produces so many great players. I remember how cricket dominated my life when I was growing up. My brothers and I would play backyard 'Tests' at home. Uncle Col would often bowl cricket balls at us, usually without warning. Watching these kids play over here my mind naturally turned to Ros and my two daughters back at home. Long separations are just part of being a cricketer I guess, but they still hurt. I understand the importance of having your parents around. I was only twelve when Dad left home. It hit me really hard as we were a very close-knit family. So it came as a double shock the following week when Mum left.

Fortunately the phone lines out of India have improved dramatically over the past few years and I was able to ring home this evening. Ros is well, although sounding a little exhausted. The renovations are proceeding slowly and according to Barry Geeton's latest estimate may not be completed until June. As I joked to Ros, at this rate the bloke might as well move in with her!

On a disappointing note, ABC Radio announced today they would no longer be broadcasting descriptions of the one-day series as the lines back to Australia were not of 'sufficient quality'. Sounds a bit odd to me. If 'quality' is a factor then how come they let Neville Oliver on air?

Day 46 ✌ (Mon April 6)

One-day International

Well, tomorrow's the big one — another match against India. Personally it's a crunch game for me as my one-day form so far has been a little average and I may not have many more opportunities to really cement my place in the team. Facing the possibility of being dropped is every cricketer's worst nightmare (that, and having a tax audit) and I was reminded of the last time I experienced a major batting slump, during the '97 Ashes tour of England. It was during this

Preparing for battle.

dark period that I read a quote from Sir Garfield Sobers: 'All batsmen have rough trots, but it will never, ever finish until he realises that he is at rock bottom.' That same day I received a phone call from Boonie asking whether I'd be interested in playing Shield cricket for Tasmania. It was then I realised I was at rock bottom.

At the team meeting we arrived at several important decisions:

1) We'd get back to basics.
2) We'd focus on each ball.
3) We'd eat Chinese (there's only so many curries a bloke can take).

As is customary on the night before a match, the team dines together as a way of all getting closer and tighter. Unfortunately the bowlers came too, but we still managed to have an enjoyable meal.

Cricket being such a mental game I decided not to join the other blokes for an after-dinner drink, preferring to psych myself up away from all distractions. So while the guys were off at some nightclub I sat down and said over and over to myself, 'You can do it, you can do it, you can do it.' It was like a form of meditation and from deep within I heard a voice say, 'Last drinks sir.' I hate it when barmen interrupt a meditation session, especially with news like that.

Day 47 ✌ (Tues April 7)

One-day International
Australia vs India

Forty thousand people packed the Green Park Stadium here in Kanpur today, all no doubt expecting to see another win for India. The authorities weren't taking any chances with security and hundreds of police armed with fire hoses were stationed along the fence, near the race and outside the Australian dressing room — anywhere they could get a good view of the game and cheer their side on.

For once we won the toss and decided to bat but unfortunately we lost both Gilly and Junior in the first few overs. Then Tugga went for a second ball duck and it was my turn to face the music. It wasn't an easy innings. The ball was moving around a bit and I spent a lot of time batting with Bevo who really likes to move between wickets, despite the heat. At one point we even ran five, of which I contributed one and Bev four. But eventually I found my rhythm, got into a groove and ended the day making 83 out of our total of 222. It wasn't a huge total but we felt it might be good enough provided we got Tendulkar cheaply, which we did, the great man holing out to Warney for just 100. But then, just as victory looked to be within reach, Ganguly stepped in with a rapid-fire 72, taking his side to victory in the 43rd over.

Once again Moody had rocks and other objects thrown at him while fielding on the boundary. He then had more objects thrown at him after the match by Tugga in response to his pathetic 0 for 26 off three overs. Not that our skipper could really be that critical. His duck today contributed to our tenth one-day loss out of eighteen matches. Typically, Tugga took the entire responsibility for our loss on his shoulders, which he shouldn't have done. As I said to him, he was only 98 per

Back in form.

cent to blame. Perhaps the one real bright spot to come out of the game today was my sensational form with the bat. I was even told that one local commentator had said something along the lines of, 'When in form Warwick Todd rates as one of the finest Australian batsmen since Bradman!' To be perfectly honest, I've always found comparisons between me and the Don a little embarrasssing. I've never been troubled by short-pitched legside bowling the way he was. Anyway, it was gratifying to hear some compliments after all the negative press written about me over the past week and I'm kind of hopeful that tomorrow's papers might just contain an apology.

Day 48 ✌ (Wed April 8)

Apology

I, Warwick Todd, formally apologise to the owners of the Landmark Hotel Kanpur for any offence or damage I may have caused last night. I accept full responsibility for the kitchen fire and agree to replace both broken windows. I further accept that the chef, his staff and family are in no way responsible for acts of terrorism in Kashmir and withdraw all such comments.

Well the pressure is sure on after yesterday's loss. We must beat Zimbabwe on Saturday to ensure a place in the finals. To tell the truth I think we're all starting to get a little sick of India and the hassles that go with touring here. Naturally we keep these sentiments to ourselves, only ever bitching about the place in private or on cable TV. But there's no doubt the team is feeling negative and this negativity is starting to creep into our training.

To me the answer is obvious — stop training. But Swampy and Tugga want us in peak condition for the next game and so it was down to the

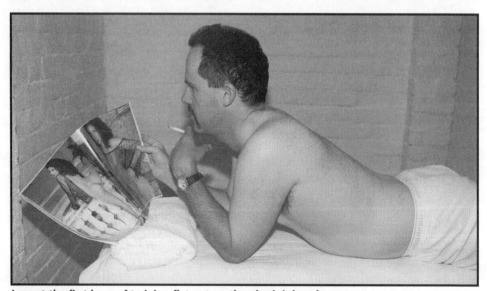

I spent the first hour of training flat out on the physio's bench.

ground this morning for yet another net session. As it turned out I spent the first hour flat out on the physio's bench, until Hooter found me and threatened to spill the beans if I didn't get out on the field.

Dinner tonight involved yet another sponsor's function, the last thing any of us felt like attending. Honestly, you get stuck on a table with these total strangers who only ever want to ask questions about cricket and what you think about the game. It gets so tedious. You could ask them questions about their lives I suppose, but they're not cricketers and are therefore boring. In the end the simplest thing is to pretend you've got a team meeting to attend and head for the hotel bar.

Day 49 ✌ (Thur April 9)

Some of the lads ventured outside the hotel this morning but as usual there was a large crowd of beggars all hassling us for a few rupees. What you've got to realise, of course, is that most beggars in India are professionals, much like teachers or journalists (only most beggars are better dressed), and giving these people money only encourages them to stay poor. On top of that, they're a bloody ungrateful lot. Take this bloke who stopped me this morning, practically tripped me over. I handed him a fifty rupee note and he refused to give me change! I don't care if he didn't have any bloody arms, I still wanted forty back.

It's funny, after so many weeks in India you get a little desensitised to the bizarre sights around you — cows wandering down the road, people relieving themselves in the middle of the street (you can't take Ponts anywhere) and all around you suicidal rickshaw drivers desperately trying to make a living. One bloke we hired for a short trip back to the hotel was nothing but skin and bone and although he peddled hard he simply couldn't make it up the hill. Eventually a half dozen or so of us got out to make it easier but he still took ages. Naturally there was no tip.

After lunch it was time to take a bus to the airport, which turned out to be a somewhat hair-raising experience. Our vehicle set off at a million miles per hour on the wrong side of the road in pouring rain, almost killing the lot of us. Eventually Swampy was persuaded to hand over the wheel but our Indian driver wasn't much better. At one point Warney became so worried he went down the front to ask the bloke to slow down, giving those of us playing cards with him a good chance to look at his hand. Brute Bernard lodged an official complaint when we arrived at the airport but all the Indians would say was that the driver was 'fully qualified'. Which over here means anyone in a brown polyester shirt.

Arriving in Delhi I was handed a copy of the *ABC Cricket Tour Book*, which featured me in their 'player profile'. It's often a worry trying to remember what answers you gave to the questions but I think I came out of this one looking pretty good.

Player Profile

Name: Warwick Todd

Favourite food: Anything parmigiana

Favourite drink: Foster's (Naturally!)

Favourite singer: John Williamson (Tugga put me on to him)

Finest moment: Scoring 127 at Leeds in 1993

Who would you invite to a party?: Chappelli, Elle McPherson, Nelson Mandela and my wife Ros

Ambition: To keep making runs for Australia

What would you do if you couldn't make runs?: Change my name to Mark Taylor! (Only kidding. Actually, I'd prefer you not to print that last bit.)

Day 50 ✌ (Fri April 10)

With a big game tomorrow there was no letting up the pace and Swampy was down at the ground at 8.30 am hitting high balls and running fielding drills. By the time the team arrived at 10.00 he was just about knackered.

One of the things we needed to sort out today was the line-up for tomorrow's clash. Basically, Moody and Damien Martyn are competing for the one spot. Tugga and Swampy were leaning towards Marto but I felt Moods was worth having, not so much for his bowling or batting but for the fact the crowd seem so intent on pelting him with objects

Relaxing by the pool during our last tour of India, with a few old faces no longer part of the Aussie squad. Note Warney up the back holding his new contract from Channel Nine. Meanwhile, I'm brushing up on some tour statistics.

his presence might deflect danger away from the rest of us. In the end, however, Moods was forced to pull out with a hamstring strain and Marto got the nod.

Back at the hotel a large package had arrived for the team containing newspapers and magazines from Australia. Being so far from home any news is greatly appreciated and the boys spent a relaxing afternoon by the pool flicking through *Sports Illustrated, Inside Sport* and *BRW*. (Actually, just the cover of *BRW*. Inside was *Bikes 'n' Babes*, a publication not likely to be approved of by Indian customs inspectors.)

Among the mail was also a pile of letters congratulating me on my sensational return to form a few days ago. That people back in Australia actually take the time to put pen to paper constantly amazes me and you can be sure that every single letter or fax receives a personal reply.

WARWICK TODD PTY LTD

Dear _____,

On behalf of Warwick, thanks for your letter/fax.

Best wishes

....
(G. Hirsh, Manager)

Of course, it's not just ordinary fans who take the trouble to write. Back in 1986 when I made my maiden Test century none other than Prime Minister Mr Bob Hawke sent me a congratulatory letter which I naturally valued very highly. In fact, it fetched $5000 at a charity auction held later that year.*

---

* I should just mention that even though the Australian Taxation Office have ruled that the Todd Family Trust is not technically a 'charity' the matter is still on appeal.

A great part of touring foreign countries is getting to know the locals.

A busy afternoon relaxing by the pool left us all very parched in the throat region and in dire need of energy replenishing fluids, which the hotel bar kindly provided. Drinks were then followed by dinner and a few quiet cocktails in the mezzanine lounge. When this closed a few of the lads were keen to kick on elsewhere but, as Tugga pointed out, it's team policy that the evening before a big match the festivities are kept within the hotel. But then Ponts (demonstrating the leadership capabilities he's no doubt blessed with) pointed out it was now after midnight and therefore technically no longer the evening before a match. Within five minutes a cab had been called and we were off.

Day 51 ✌ (Sat April 11)

Australia vs Zimbabwe

With an important match scheduled for today the last thing I felt like this morning was picking up a pen and spending half an hour signing my name, but this was the amount of paperwork required by New Dehli's chief Bail Justice before my release could be arranged. Then it was off to the tiny Feroz Shah Kotla Ground, the scene of today's game. After our customary warm-up, involving a short net session, a few throw downs and a bit of wet towel flicking back in the rooms, Tugga gathered us together and spoke about the importance of the match, how we had to beat Zimbabwe in order to make the final. Our skipper then spoke about mental toughness, a theme he often stresses.

Just reminding Tugga of his recent form.

According to Tugga, the key to success is not letting any negative thoughts enter your head. 'Like the fact we've only won eight out of eighteen games since you took over as captain,' I added, just in case any of the younger blokes needed an example of what a 'negative thought' might be.

Fortunately we won the toss and our openers Junior (87) and Ponts (145) got us off to a flying start. I wasn't required to bat which was just as well because, for the first time since arriving in India, the old tummy was playing up. I've been so lucky in this respect throughout my career. On our last tour here for the World Cup in '96 I only suffered one bad bout of diarrhoea, and that cleared up by late '97. But I think I may have pushed my luck last night, tucking into a huge meal at New Dehli's only sushi restaurant. Anyway, I spent most of our innings driving the porcelain bus while out on the field the boys made it through to a pretty impressive total of 3 for 294.

As expected, the Zimbabwe lads came out determined to do well and, sure enough, the Flower brothers started putting together a solid partnership, reaching 121 runs in just 18 overs. But once again the inexperienced opposition were no match for us, especially in the area of psychological pressure. Tugga, Bev and myself were all brought in close to offer a variety of 'pleasantries' in the direction of the two batsmen. Now despite what some people think, sledging, or 'chirping' as the South Africans call it, involves much more than just mindless abuse. It can be used cunningly to unsettle an oppenent. For example, if a bloke is not hitting the ball well outside the off stump it might be useful to say something to this effect, such as, 'You f*#king poofter.' It certainly worked today and we eventually had the Zimbabwe boys all out for 278, 16 runs short of victory.

There were quite a few positives to emerge from today's win, not the least of which was a general lift in our energy output and intensity, not so much on the field but certainly during the post-match singalong. Ponts also took Man of the Match for his sensational 145, the equal highest score by an Australian in a one-day international. It's great to see Ponts bounce back after all the negative press and publicity he's received in recent weeks and it would have been a fitting tribute to his talent and new-found maturity to see him accept the Man of the Match award personally. Unfortunately he'd already left for a nightclub.

On a sour note, Warney strained his already injured shoulder attempting a catch at cover and lay motionless on the dressing room bench for thirty minutes after the match. Hours later he could barely raise his arm above horizontal, a situation that could spell the end for him as an Australian cricketer. He might still be able to bowl but golf would almost certainly be an impossibilty. On top of this, Tugga's fears about a player being injured by projectiles were realised today with Damien Martyn copping an empty beer bottle to the back of the head. Although the incident happened on our team bus and Gilly later apologised, it underscores the danger faced by today's cricketers.

Day 52 ✌ (Sun April 12)

More sightseeing was on the agenda today, with a trip organised to India's famous Taj Mahal. Normally I avoid anywhere that's not air-conditioned but this is an amazing monument and one I was keen to see. Unfortunately it involved us fronting up in the hotel lobby at 5.45 am which meant leaving the Ashok nightclub early, but in the end it was worth it. The Taj really is one of the wonders of the modern world, up there with the great pyramids of Egypt and Melbourne's Crown Casino. It was constructed by Emperor Shah Jahan for his wife and took twenty-one years to finish. (He must have been using Geeton Constructions.) The central part of the building is a marble mausoleum and the echo under its soaring dome is superb. You could hear our cries of 'Aussie Aussie Aussie, oy oy oy' for just about miles.

Two special views of the Taj Mahal. That's me, on the right.

And, as it turned out, this was tonight's dinner.

The team dinner tonight was a low-key affair, and quite pleasant, despite the in-house sitar player. (Has anyone ever thought of actually tuning those instruments?) I believe we're finally starting to mesh as a team. The new guys have all slotted in well and only a few players still have to wear name tags. Marto and some bowler from Brisbane. There was one quite humorous moment, when our waiter announced tonight's special was 'pork vindaloo'. Quick as a flash I piped up with 'And if we eat it we'll all be in the loo!'

It went down so well I might just work it into my sportsmen's night routine.

Day 53 ✌ (Mon April 13)

People openly relieving themselves in the Ganges. Not a pretty sight.

Amazing scenes on the telly today, with the local news showing three million people bathing in the Ganges as part of some religious festival. The Ganges is of course considered a holy river by Hindus but to be perfectly blunt, the place is one big sewer. It's dirty, smelly and full of rubbish, sort of like Bondi Beach after rain. Families live on the river, wash their clothes in it and, despite it being 'holy', openly relieve themselves along the banks. Not a pretty sight.

The final training session before a big match is always important and we like to re-create match conditions as closely as possible. Just for added realism, during fielding drill Swampy pelted Moods with rocks from down on the boundary.

Heading back to the hotel on the bus I was amazed to see the number of billboards featuring Indian cricketers backing products and causes. Players like Tendulkar obviously get paid a fortune to promote soft drinks and beer while Saurav Ganguly is actually a spokesman for the threatened Bengal tiger. Of course, he's not the first cricketer to have been involved with an animal welfare issue.

Personally I'm all for promoting products but I'm wary about lending the name Todd to anything remotely political. A little while back I was approached by the Wilderness Society in Australia which wanted someone to front their campaign over logging on the New South Wales southern coast. This was an issue quite close to my heart as my family owned a block of land in the area that we'd been wanting to clear-fell for years, only to be blocked by council by-laws, so I was keen to get involved. It was only after I'd posed for the poster and they'd printed about 10 000 'Warwick Todd says, "Join the Green Team"', stickers that I realised they were *against* logging. They ended up having to pulp the bloody lot. I also maintain a pretty strict line over endorsing products. I refuse to promote anything I wouldn't actually use myself. So you'll never see W Todd flogging exercise equipment.

At the team meeting we agreed it was time to get back to basics. We also had a good long chat about the Indian batsmen and what would be the best place to bowl at them. Most of us agreed the WACA. Tugga then spoke about the need for our top order to get a start, to really put pressure on the Indian team. After this we all agreed it was time to get back to basics. I feel the team meetings could be getting a little repetitive.

Warwick Todd says, 'Hit gun laws for six!' Vote One — Australian Shooters Party

Day 54 ✌ (Tues April 14)

Australia vs India — Final

Well, this is it, the big one. The Pepsi Cup Final. And arriving at the tiny Feroz Shah Kotla Ground in New Delhi it looked like the entire country had turned up to watch the match. Queues stretched for miles outside the ground with desperate fans being pushed and beaten by baton-wielding police. I honestly haven't seen such brutality since my last coaching stint at the Australian Cricket Academy.

No changes to the team today except for Damien Martyn, who was named 12th man. Marto was obviously disappointed at being over-looked for the final but I'll speak to him tonight, tell him to keep hanging in there and that his chance will come in Sharjah. Hopefully he'll swallow it.

I haven't seen such brutality since my last coaching stint at the Australian Cricket Academy.

India won the toss and so, after a short warm-up, there was nothing for it but to wish each other luck, pump a few anti-inflammatories into Warney, and get out onto the field. Despite a slow start our bowlers soon found rhythm and got rid of the dangerous Ganguly for just 29. This brought the even more dangerous Tendulkar to the wicket. At the meeting last night we'd discussed strategies for handling the dashing stroke maker. We figured that he'd naturally be expecting a bit of the usual chat from those of us close in and that this could well have the effect of inspiring him. So we opted for reverse psychology and decided to give him the old silent treatment. Three or maybe even four balls went by before one of the boys cracked and called him a poofter. After that it was on for young and old. Flem eventually knocked him over for 15. Aided by Kaspa, Moody and even Tugga (two wickets), we eventually had the home team all out for just 227.

Our innings got off to a shaky start with Gilly out for just 1, but Junior and Ponts soon steadied the ship. At 3 down Tugga decided to send Warney in as a pinch-hitter, a move that seemed to be working until he was bowled by a full toss bean-ball that flicked the top of his stumps. Now anyone who knows anything about one-day cricket (and this excludes both umpires) will know that any fast delivery over waist high should be called a no-ball. Naturally Warney stood his ground waiting for the umpire to say something but the only call that came was from me in the dressing room yelling 'That's a no-ball you blind ar*#hole!' Fortunately Tugga managed to keep the run rate up with a rapid-fire 57 and Bev contributed a superb 75. I joined him with just 23 runs required off 7 overs, not a big task but still one to be approached with caution — teams have fallen for less. (I know, I've had money on them to do so.) I'll never forget the final over, I was on strike to off-spinner Hrishikesh Kanitkar, and he dropped one a little short. The natural temptation was to dance down the pitch and put him away for a boundary but years of international experience have taught me that was a no-win option. If I missed the ball I'd be stumped. And if I scored the runs I'd be too far down the pitch to have

The winners! A tip: It's wise to hold off drinking until after the team photo.

any chance of souveniring a stump. So I squeezed a quick single, let Bev hit the winning runs and walked off with three stumps for my next testimonial year auction.

It was a wonderful victory from a team that no one really believed could win and naturally we partied pretty hard after the game. Tugga was named Man of the Match (57 runs and two wickets), and watching him stagger forward to collect the award was a special moment. The Indian players were understandably a little shell-shocked over losing the final but to their credit dropped by our rooms and ended up sharing in the celebrations for quite a few hours. Until their manager demanded we unlock the door and let them out.

Day 55 ✌ (Wed April 15)

Last night is still a blur for many of us, what with the celebrations over our stunning finals victory. Obviously people were just as excited by the win as we were, judging from the endless round of media commitments. During the evening I was interviewed by everyone: radio, TV, press and a stipendiary magistrate who seemed obsessed with finding out how those three cows found their way onto the team bus.

The only people not carried away by our win were the Indian fans, most still stunned by their team's defeat. Reading the paper this morning revealed that one Bombay supporter was so upset with India losing that he fired a shotgun into his television before turning the weapon on himself. It brings home just how seriously local fans take the game over here, when you think that some-one could get so carried away they'd actually damage a TV.

A lot of media interest has centred on Warney and his decision to play in Sharjah, rather than return for treatment on his injured shoulder. The fact of the matter is, no Australian player likes to see his place in the team taken by someone else. We play for the love of the game, for the baggy green, and there's no way a player would willingly miss out on the chance to represent his country. Or the ten grand prize-money on offer.

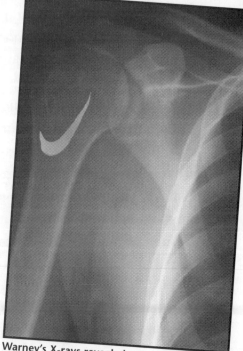

Warney's X-rays revealed some interesting results.

Day 56 ✌ (Thurs April 16)

The brief flight across to Sharjah went without incident and we soon checked into the team hotel, where we were joined by our new coach for the tournament, Allan Border. Much has been written over the years about Australia's number one run-scorer, with people who have never met the man declaring him gruff, aloof and antisocial. In my experience nothing could be further from the truth. AB always loved sitting down and having a beer in the rooms after a game. Provided of course no one else was there.

AB shares another laugh.

At the team meeting plans for the upcoming tournament were discussed, in particular our injury worries, the heavy schedule ahead of us (four matches in five days) and the fact that Sharjah is a 'dry' or alcohol-free state. In the end it was decided to rotate the squad as much as possible, with eleven blokes playing, two being rested and one making a daily trip into neighbouring Dubai to pick up beer.

After dinner I made a call home to speak with my daughter Raleisha, who celebrated her eighth birthday a few days ago. She was obviously excited to hear from her dad and told me she'd been busy taking photos around the house with the new camera Ros and I gave her. In fact, she's already sent me across a few shots which I'm looking forward to receiving tomorrow.

Day 57 ✌ (Fri April 17)

Dear Daddy
    thank you for my
birthday present. I enjoy
taking photos with it.
Mummy says hello.
    Love Raleisha X

■ SPORTS NEWS IN BRIEF

Aussie Withdraws!

By Shimar Sidhalmar

AAP. Australian cricketer Warwick Todd today made a surprise exit from the one-day squad here in Sharjah. No reason for his sudden withdrawal was given but it is believed to involve a family matter back in Australia.

Home for Winter

Despite a lot of press speculation that I left the Australian tour of Sharjah because of 'marital problems', nothing could be further from the truth. As it turned out, that 'incriminating' photo was basically a silly mix-up, something Ros explained when I returned home. What happened was she had simply gone into the bedroom where our builder Barry Geeton was doing some painting to find him passed out on the bed from the fumes. Thinking nothing of her own safety Ros flung off her clothes (to avoid getting them covered in Dulux gloss enamel) and proceeded to offer mouth-to-mouth. Raleisha must have heard Barry groan as he came to and rushed in with her camera. Simple explanation.

The real reason I returned prematurely was that my old knee injury had flared up again and no amount of anti-inflammatories, pain-killers or Victoria Bitter seemed to be working. Shortly after returning to Australia I made an appointment with the Australian team's orthopaedic surgeon who was blunt in his assessment: 'You're pissed'. I made another appointment the next week in which he told me, 'Either you have an operation or you forget about ever playing cricket again'. Well, I tell you, that news hit pretty hard. The thought that I might never pull on the baggy green cap again was enough to send my world into a spin. However, operations scare the hell out of me and I decided to seek a second opinion. I went to the top knee man in Sydney, and another in Perth, I spoke with two in Melbourne but they all said the same thing: 'No, we can't operate for free in return for an ad'. It was around this time that a friend recommended I forget the doctors and see a chiropractor. Now I'll admit, I was initially very sceptical, viewing chiropractors as being part of the 'lunatic fringe' of the medical world. Still, the knee was no better and I had nothing to lose so I went along to see Kevin McKeown at his inner-city practice. I walked in to find the waiting room full, always a good sign — a full house says something positive about the practitioner. Turned out Kevin shared rooms with a masseuse who offered some pretty 'extensive' services and I was his only patient for the day. Or for the week, as it turned out. Anyway, he got me up on the bench and within thirty seconds declared my left knee was showing obvious signs of ligament torsion with marked posterior lateral resection. Which came as a real blow as my right knee was the one giving me trouble. Anyway, he gave me a thorough workout using heat, ultrasound and stretching techniques but sadly, despite repeated visits, there was no real improvement in the knee. The only positive to come out of the whole experience was the fact these visits didn't cost me a cent.

By May things were looking really grim. My knee was so sore that even getting up to the fridge was a painful experience and the thought of making Australia's June training camp just a distant dream. I must say, Ros was fabulous throughout this whole dark period. There would be times when I came home pretty down, grumpy and non-communicative. Not once did she snap back or complain. I guess the fact she'd gone to Surfers Paradise with an old school friend for six weeks helped, but her postcards were all very supportive.

Despite living with constant pain I still managed to main-

The 'Toddy 2000' — as seen on *Good Morning Australia*.

tain my busy media and promotional schedule. In addition to sportsmen's nights and the odd motivational talk I was kept busy promoting my latest range of fitness equipment, the Toddy 2000. It's a fully patented (and partially tested) space-age device designed for those who want maximum fitness with minimum effort and I was pleased to spear-head a national sales campaign.

Charity work also kept me busy throughout the middle of the year. Being a modest person this is a side to Warwick Todd that I'm naturally keen to play down, especially my involvement with Uncle Ron's Seaside Camp for Boys which — as I explained to the police — was done purely as an ambassador. I never once attended the camps or took part in any of the 'hokey-pokey' sessions later described in court. But I still do a lot of charity work — selfless, behind-the-scenes contributions. As a high-profile sportsman I believe I have a duty to give of myself. To be honest, I find it hard to say no. Just last week I hosted a charity auction for some street kids foundation which raised $20000. Deduct my nominal appearance fee and a few minor expenses and

Tugga and me at a Calcutta leper hospital. Naturally I took a few precautions.

those homeless youth are now $12 000 better off. Even during the tour of India I often went out of my way to help the less fortunate, be they beggars, cripples or just Gavin Robertson. No request was too much trouble, even the day Steve Waugh and I were asked to visit a local leper hospital.

But for all the 'inner glow' I felt from helping others, the niggling pain in my right knee refused to go away. If I was to stand any chance of making the Australian squad for the Commonwealth Games in September I would have to go under the knife. One cold, wet morning in late May I checked into a private sports clinic in Double Bay.

Naturally I don't remember much about the day of the operation. Like I said, hospitals and needles scare the living daylights out of me. According to my anaesthetist at one point I was screaming and thrashing around at him so wildly I had to be restrained. This happened in the hospital car park when he pinched a spot right in front of me. Shortly after I was in the operating theatre and experiencing the full joy of

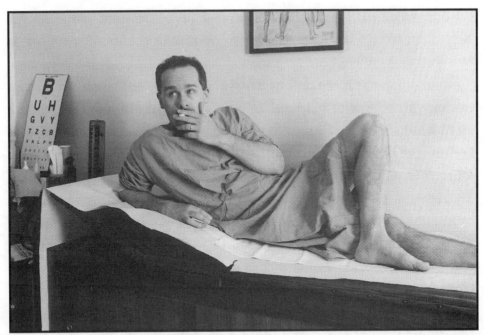

One last gasper before going under the knife.

major knee surgery. According to my specialist Mr Michael Bennings the operation went smoothly, though how he'd know is anyone's guess. He was in Noosa at a medical conference on the day and the procedure was handled by his junior associate. Whatever the case, I woke up the next day feeling like death. The first thing I remember seeing was the smiling face of Ros. She'd left a photo of herself on the bedside table before rushing off to visit a sick aunt in Noosa. My knee was heavily bandaged and they had me on pretty high doses of pain-killers, but even so the slightest movement almost sent me through the roof. Even getting up to take a leak was out of the question and I was forced to relieve myself lying down in bed, something I hadn't done since the night in July 1997 when we celebrated winning the Ashes.

The following days and weeks were not easy but slowly I regained my strength. I couldn't have done it without the help of my physio Deb Kendall, whose constant support and encouragement saw me through some pretty dark days. The rehabilitation schedule was gruelling. At one point I was seeing Deb four times a week (though Fridays were just for a drink). I also received enormous support from everyone on the Australian team who, realising how important this rehabilitation period was for me, kept well away.

In addition to physio and traditional medicine I also visited a natural healer who offered to help me on a psycho-spiritual plane. I reckon a lot of what she said was mumbo-jumbo but as she was a friend of Ros's I felt sort of obliged to go along. Basically she explained that there are four types of people in the world. I'm a Wolf and I should therefore avoid cheese. Or cheese-based products. I'm not certain of which as I only went once and the taped rainforest sounds were a little distracting.

Throughout these dark winter days I had just one goal, or two if you count resuming line-dancing classes, and that was making the team training camp in September. It was here that the teams for both the Commonwealth Games and the tour of Pakistan would be selected. Deb thought I was crazy and that I'd be lucky to make the World Cup next year, but I had a goal and I worked towards it. I knew that if I could just handle a solid session in the nets without any pain then I'd be ready to play. Of course, it wasn't easy. For every step forward there were two steps back. But by early August I'd achieved my goal of moving freely in the nets. By the end of that month I'd even stopped using a bedpan. Time once again to get back in the baggy green...

The Lead-up ✌ (Fri 4 Sept)

Australian Squad Training Camp

Today the twenty-one best cricketers in Australia, along with Adam Dale and Damien Martyn, gathered in Brisbane for a team training camp. With the Commonwealth Games just a few days away followed by a tough tour of Pakistan, it was time to regroup, shake off the cobwebs and shed a little of that winter weight. Not that we'd exactly been allowed to 'slack off' on the fitness front since returning from India. As usual Swampy set us all an intensive off-season exercise program, calling for some pretty big gym sessions. How does 700 sit-ups sound to you? Naturally we weren't expected to do all 700 in a row, rest breaks were permitted. I'd generally do ten, take a month or so off, then do another ten.

Cricket will be played for the first time at these Commonwealth Games and many different teams are competing. Unfortunately not all countries seem to be treating the tournament with the respect it deserves — in particular, Pakistan and India, which are sending decidedly B-grade teams. England are not even sending a team at all, a move that could well provide them with their best international result in years. Mind you, sitting out the tournament won't do their prospects much good in the future. We thrashed them last year and I can't see them doing any better against us this summer. If you ask me the major problem for the Poms is that they lack mental toughness. There's no 'edge' to their game, no competitive intensity. I played a season for Norwich a few years back* and every match was like a

---

* Details of which can be found in my best-selling tour diary *Pimms, Poms and Poofters* (ABC Books, 1993).

pleasant social hit-out. No passion, no sledging, everyone in the team liked everyone else. That's where we Aussies have the edge — deep down we all hate each other.

But if a few other countries are not taking the Games seriously we Aussies, in particular our captain Tugga, are very keen to do well in a tournament that may never be repeated, hence this three-day camp. And don't be fooled by the word 'camp' and start conjuring up images of sitting round fires singing 'Ging Gang Gooly'. From the moment we arrived today it was hard slog, starting with a practice match against the Cricket Academy who ended up beating us by 30 runs! To be fair, though, many of our boys had just stepped off the plane from England (where Australia A had been touring) and were still battling the combined effects of jet lag and alcohol poisoning.

After the match I was given the privilege of taking part in a small modelling assignment...

Australian bowler Glenn McGrath and designer Grace Ng-Spyrou model the successful new Commonwealth Games uniform.

Australian batsman Warwick Todd models one of the losing designs.

Practice Match 2 ✌ (Sat 5 Sept)

Another practice match today, this time against NSW at Buderim, saw us win by a comfortable 130 runs. I was particularly happy with my form, striking the ball well as I raced to a quick-fire 50. So you can imagine my disappointment when I sat down at lunch and saw an article in the *Courier-Mail* questioning my place in the Commonwealth Games squad. Not surprisingly the journalist involved was Ray Sturt who has been leading the 'anti-Todd' push for years. It's the same old 'destabilising influence' argument he's always trotting out but I'll be honest — it really annoys me. Look, I have no problem if a cricketing expert (or Ray Sturt) wants to question my form, or some technical aspect of my game. That's fine. But when you're attacked on a *personal* level it's a different matter. I know things can't be easy for Ray since his wife ran off with a graphic designer from the *Weekend Magazine,* but I do wish he wouldn't let this bitterness affect his writing.

Saturday night saw most of us head into town for a few quiet beers. We attracted quite a bit of attention from local cricket fans all keen to meet their heroes. I guess a lot of people don't realise the pressure we members of the Aussie team live under, the constant focus on us in this sports-mad country of ours. I mean, the average bloke can throw on a pair of old tracky daks, go out and have a few drinks, maybe get into a fight, spend the night in a police cell and no one really cares. But that sort of behaviour is simply out of the question for us members of the Australian cricket team. We have to wait until we're overseas on tour.

Practice Match 3 ✌ (Sun 6 Sept)

Another practice match, our third in as many days. This time we took on a rather out-of-form New Zealand team in front of a 4000 strong crowd. Tugga decided to rest himself and so Junior led us on to the ground. The Kiwis got off to a flying start, reaching 0 for 90 before our two spinners Gavin Robertson and Brad Young stepped in with three wickets each. Robbo in particular bowled brilliantly and has come along in leaps and bounds since his debut in India. I know for a fact he learnt much from that tour, speaking with many former Indian spin greats and seeking their advice. Despite what they said he obviously decided to keep playing and it paid dividends today. With New Zealand restricted to just 151 runs we had little trouble reaching the target for the loss of one wicket. Junior delighted the crowd by slamming 98 off just 63 balls. I guess some might have seen this display as being a little 'selfish', given there were half-a-dozen other players waiting by for the opportunity of a little batting practice while Wonder Boy got his kicks hitting a B-grade team all over an undersized pitch. But you certainly won't hear any such criticism from me.

Off the field there was disappointing news that Sri Lanka was withdrawing its best players from the Commonwealth Games after a row over their sponsor's logo. The Sri Lankans will now be leaving behind Sanath Jayasuriya, Aravinda de Silva, Arjuna Ranatunga (which will at least avoid problems with excess baggage penalties on the flight over) and controversial bowler/chucker Muthiah Muralidaran. This means that the only countries really sending full-strength teams are Australia, New Zealand and Zimbabwe, in as much as Zimbabwe can ever be called full strength. On a positive note, the players' committee announced tonight that they'd finally come up with a suitable nickname for new boy Brad Young — 'Youngie'. Only took them three days.

Day 1 ✌ (Mon 7 Sept)

Brisbane airport, early afternoon and as the boys gathered yet again for another overseas tour I remember thinking, 'Here we go'. Actually, I remember singing 'Here we go' along with a few other team favourites as we boarded the flight. Now, it's been a long time since an Australian cricket team has travelled economy class but I think it says something about our commitment and professionalism that not a single complaint was heard, until the plane took off and we really put the foot down. Eventually all members of the team were given an up-grade (though I'm not sure Ponts yelling 'Hey guys, follow me up front' technically constitutes an upgrade), and the flight proceeded without incident. Naturally a few cleansing ales were enjoyed en route and by the time we touched down in KL one member of our squad (who shall remain nameless) was so off his nut we had to sign his customs declaration for him. And if you think that sounds easy, try spelling 'Kasprowicz'. Not that I was exactly stone-cold sober myself. I remember emerging from the duty-free shop with about $1000 worth of CD-Roms and computer games only to realise I don't own a computer! Thank God I hadn't paid for any of them.

Speaking of 'payment', none of us on this tour will be getting a cent, not even travel allowance. Compare this to our star paceman Glenn 'Pigeon' McGrath who did a groin (his own) at the training camp and is now sitting back collecting $2000 a week in injury money. Interestingly, any Malaysian athlete who wins gold has been promised a life insurance policy worth 50,000 Malaysian ringgit (about $2.50 Australian).

We soon arrived at the Games Village, the Vista Komonwel, a drab high-rise complex packed full of athletes. Already quite a few of the Australians there were complaining about the crowded conditions, competitors packed four or five to a room, tiny bunks, bathrooms shared by dozens of people. Fortunately one of Australia's junior Commonwealth Games officials came to the rescue, saying he had a bit of room on the mezzanine level of his suite back at the Palace of the Golden Horses that might just house the swimming team if a few of them didn't mind going without en-suites.

Despite the overcrowding and a few other problems like lack of air-conditioning and the odd rat, there was a real buzz in the air. Little wonder really, when you've got 316 of Australia's top athletes (321 if you count the lawn bowlers) all together, all focused on taking out a gold medal.

After we'd checked in the Australian flag was raised, accompanied by numerous renditions of 'Advance Australia Fair', a song rarely heard in cricketing circles. According to one bloke I met it's our national anthem, but I'll have to check that out. Another tune getting a fair workout on the in-house PA was the official Games song, containing the catchy chorus:

And now, Malaysia: Comes the real test.
Rise up, Malaysia; Run with all our zest.

To which we humorously added:

Shut up Malaysia, you're starting to annoy.
Piss off Malaysia, Aussie oy oy oy!

After a formal apology had been issued to the head of Malaysia's Commonwealth Games Committee (how were we to know he was at the flag-raising?) a meeting of all Australian athletes was called. We were briefed by Chef de Mission Don Stockins, who spoke about our expected image and attitude over here. According to him we Australians are here to 'win with style and humility, and to lose with grace'. Blah, blah, blah, we've heard it all before. About the only thing of interest explained at the meeting was the drug situation. Malaysia is of course very strict on illegal substances and according to Stockins any athlete caught with recreational drugs risks being flogged or even

A proud moment for Australia at the Games Village.

given the death penalty. You could tell a lot of Aussies were pretty taken aback by this but for those of us cricketers who remember playing under Simmo they were actually pretty standard penalties — you'd get worse for missing the team bus. Routine drug-testing will be carried out extensively here in Kuala Lumpur and just about every competitor can expect to be asked for a urine sample. Some of this will be tested, the rest — judging from the beer I had this afternoon — will be sent to a local brewery.

Day 2 ✌ (Tues 8 Sept)

Day Two in Malaysia and more complaints are emerging about conditions here at the Games Village, with many athletes unhappy about having to share rooms. Hard to know what they're complaining about — I'm having to share with Steve Waugh. There's actually three of us in Room 114, me, Tugga and a rat we're yet to name.

Down at breakfast the news emerged of a scandal sure to send the international cricketing world into a spin. And for once it doesn't involve me. Apparently an internal Pakistan inquiry has found Salim Malik, Wasim Akram and Ijaz Ahmed (hereafter to be known as 'the slimy Paki bastards') guilty of trying to rig matches. Of course, these allegations are nothing new, they first emerged back in '94 when Warney, Junior and Tim May claimed they were each offered $US200 000 ($9.2 billion Australian) by Pakistan's Salim Malik to throw a game. At the time the Aussie trio were called 'liars', 'racists' and 'poor sports' — claims I now regret making but I was writing a newspaper column at the time and simply needed to fill some space. The boys' claims were eventually made public and the matter heard by an independent Pakistani judge whose ruling was unequivocal: 'Salim is innocent — my nephew would never do a thing like this'. What really shocks us as a team is the thought that we may unwittingly have played in a rigged match. It was the Singer Cup back in 1994 during which the Pakis fell short of our modest 180 run target. Out of interest I looked up the scorecard from that game...

Scoreboard

PAKISTAN

SAEEED c MGrath b S Waugh	46
SOHAIL ht wkt b McGrath	0
UL-HAQ ht wkt b Warne	0
BASIT ht wkt b Warne	0
MALIK c and b and ht wkt b S Waugh	22
LATIF (retired hurt)	107
AKRAM ht wkt b McGrath	0
RAZA ht wkt b McDermott	0
WAQAR ht wkt b Warne	0
MUSHTAQ ht wkt b McDermott	0
MUJTABA not out	1
Extras	2
TOTAL	178

Believe it or not, this earnt me a two match suspension. All I was trying to do was indicate to the umpire where the ball hit me. He still insisted I was lbw.

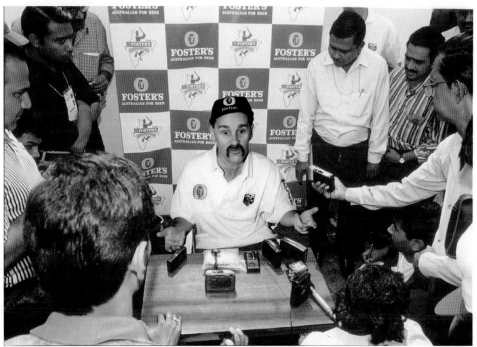

As a senior player I'm often called upon to say a few words at press conferences. Usually 'I'm sorry...'

Facilites on the sub-continent have improved dramatically in recent years. Many of the dressing rooms even have running water.

Mind you, their corporate boxes could still use a little work.

We all have our own ways of warming up.

Some of the guys hone their reflexes by boxing. Others take it a little easier.

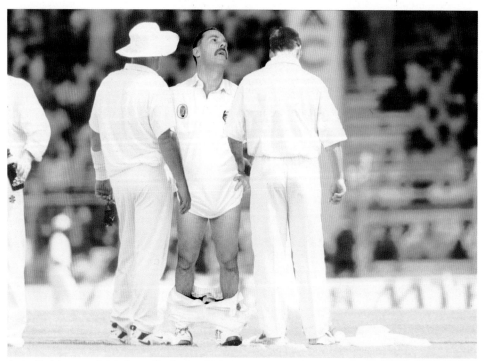

In India it's essential to beat the heat whatever way you can.

And replacing lost fluids is vital.

At the time nothing seemed suspicious but looking back at the stats it's pretty obvious something was a bit fishy. I mean, really, when has Tugga ever dismissed an opening batsman?

The other extraordinary thing about the whole scandal is that it involves not just 'average' players but two former captains. Captains of a Test team! Can you imagine Tubby Taylor walking out on to a ground and deliberately failing with the bat? While certain aspects of this mental picture may ring true, there's no way an Aussie skipper would ever sink so low.

The question of punishment is an interesting one. Former Aussie

Salim Malik in Sydney indicating how many grand he got for making a first ball duck at the SCG.

legend Allan Border has called for all Pakistani players found guilty of match-fixing to be banned from playing cricket for life as an 'absolute minimum'. I differ slightly. Having played cricket in Pakistan I think any of their players found guilty should be forced to continue playing there for the term of their natural life. You won't find a much greater deterrent than that.

After breakfast a few of us decided to take a stroll round the Games Village. It's a new sensation being housed with so many other Australian athletes and we were keen to organise a card game or maybe get a game of touch footy going but the place was absolutely deserted. Turned out everyone was off at training. It was the same last night when Bev and I tried organising a pub crawl. With three days still to go before the Opening Ceremony I think a few competitors are taking things a little too seriously.

Day 3 ✌ (Wed 9 Sept)

Our first game today, a preliminary match against Canada. Naturally most experts were predicting it should be a walkover but Tugga was taking nothing for granted, insisting we all be at the ground at least five minutes before play. In reality, the main 'enemy' today will be the heat. The average temperature at this time of year is 34 degrees and the humidity hovers round 95 per cent. Not exactly ideal conditions for a sporting event, especially when combined with the sort of smog and exhaust fumes you get round a big city like KL. Interestingly, despite the heat and recent fires Malaysian officials claim there have been no dangerous pollution readings since January, which coincidentally was the month they stopped taking pollution readings.

Down at the Kalab Aman ground Tugga won the toss and decided to send the Canadians in, with Flem given the honour of bowling the first ball in Commonwealth Games cricket history, followed by the first lbw appeal which was unfortunately turned down. I naturally muttered a few quiet sentiments in the direction of the umpire on the accuracy of his decision to become the first player in Commonwealth Games cricket history reported to a match referee. Quite an historic few minutes. But eventually we settled down to business, easily dismissing the Canada boys for 60 runs, their top scorer being Sundries (23). After a quick break Junior and Gilly went out to bat, the latter actually falling to a pretty average bowler called Thurasingham for just 17. Naturally our embarrassed opener copped a fair ribbing from the boys as he walked off, and rightly so — Canada are little better than a club grade side — but Ponts quickly steadied the ship and together with Junior knocked off the required runs in 14 overs.

With the game finishing early I took the opportunity of jumping in a cab and heading into town for a bit of sightseeing. It's an impressive

There was no thought about any of us not taking this match seriously.

city Kuala Lumpur with some very up-market shops and hotels. Like all Asian cities there's a slum district but even here I found the people very proud and dignified. What they lack in wealth they more than make up for in poverty. They're a very gentle race, the Malaysians, but they will snap if pushed. I must say it was refreshing not to be recognised constantly. Sometimes the pressure of always being under the spotlight can get to you, people stopping to talk, wanting autographs etc. I guess it's just the price of fame. If I wasn't a top international cricketer but just a normal person, say 'Joe Average' or 'Justin Langer', then I could probably go anywhere without being hassled. But there's no getting away completely from the fans and back at the Games Village we cricketers were yet again the centre of attention, signing autographs and chatting with other athletes keen to catch a glimpse of an elite sporting unit. One young bloke, obviously a local, was very keen to meet us and play a bit of cricket. So we found a nearby park and I rolled the arm over a few times, watching him swing and miss. I honestly don't think he had a clue about the game but I'm always happy to spend time with young fans. It was only later someone told me he was captain of the Malaysian cricket team.

Day 4 ✌ (Thur 10 Sept)

Another rest day for us cricketers, but there was still plenty to do here as spectators at the Games. Last night we went along to see the Aussie hockey team play India and this morning a few of us dropped by to watch the lawn bowling. It was the women's singles team, headed by Roma Dunn who, at just fifty-five, represents the younger face of this exciting sport.

The afternoon was spent relaxing with a few of the boys at the Games Village — and of course the girls. It's taken a bit of getting used to, sharing sporting facilities with the fairer sex. Usually cricket tours are men-only affairs and you can often go for months without even speaking to a woman, unless she's serving behind a bar. This, of course,

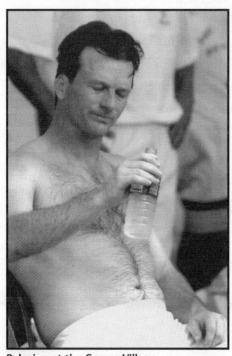

Relaxing at the Games Village.

is changing with more wives and girlfriends now accompanying the Aussie team on long tours, such as the Ashes. And I think this is great — not only do the ladies provide a stabilising, civilising effect, they can also caddy for us on golf days.

A few quiet gins and tonic rounded out a perfect day, but all good things must come to an end and, you guessed it, 6.00 was team meeting time. I snuck in a little late and sat up the back as the usual spiel was delivered: commitment, hard yards, team spirit. Then it was announced that Grant Hackett would be swimming the second leg of the 200 metres. I suddenly realised I was in the wrong team meeting. I should have noticed straightaway — everyone there was drinking water.

By the time I made it to the correct room Tugga had already done the 'commitment, hard yards, team spirit' talk and was having a lie down while our coach Swampy Marsh set about trying to explain the ACB's strict new racial and religious vilification policy. Under this policy 'no player will engage in any conduct, act towards or speak to any other player in a manner which offends, insults, humiliates, intimidates, threatens, disparages or vilifies the other player on the basis of that player's race, religion, colour, descent or national or ethnic origin'. Came across as a lot of legal mumbo-jumbo to me but the basic thrust seemed to be that we can no longer call, say, a Paki player a 'turban-headed, curry-munching, bribe-taking, ball-tampering, wife-beating, match-fixing black poofter bastard'. The word 'black' must now be removed.

Speaking of blacks, I heard a great joke in the dining hall tonight:

Q: Why are abos called 'boongs'?
A: Because that's the sound they make when they hit your bullbar.

Beauty, eh? And I'm sure Arthur Tunstall won't mind me repeating it here.

Day 5 ✌ (Fri 11 Sept)

More disorganisation today with the bus taking us to the ground for a practice session failing to arrive at the village. It wasn't such a bad thing though, as we all appreciated the chance for a morning off. The social schedule here in KL has been pretty hectic, with all the athletes warming to the task of enjoying themselves to the max. Having so many youngsters of both sexes living side by side in this steamy environment, naturally there's been a fair bit of 'fraternising'. Provided it's all kept low-key and there are no weight-lifters involved I don't have a problem with this but I have learnt from experience that you have to be very careful. Many years ago in my bachelor days I toured England with an Australian Youth Squad. After a match in Sussex I got drinking with a local lass, a dental nurse (though that's not actually relevant). One thing led to another and we ended up back at the team hotel. Two days later I was shocked to be told the woman involved was threatening to press charges against me for sexual assault. The fact was I did not force that woman to do anything and our twenty-seven minutes together were purely consensual. Fortunately for me there were three other members of the team sharing my room that night so I had plenty of witnesses and no charges were laid, but it highlighted the dangers of sporting tour liaisons.

Tomorrow is our first 'serious' match of the tournament, against an Antiguan team led by Ritchie Richardson and featuring the fearsome bowling talents of one Curtly Ambrose who, despite being almost thirty-five, is still a very frightening opponent. It will be particularly interesting to see Tugga and Curtly face to face on a cricket field again, reviving memories of their infamous 1995 clash in Trinidad when the big West Indian paceman had to be forcibly restrained from hitting Steve Waugh. (Mind you, most of us in the Aussie squad have had to

be forcibly restrained from hitting Steve Waugh at one time or another.) But this incident certainly created headlines and I remember the whole thing clearly as I was batting with Tugga at the time. Curtly had just delivered a searing bouncer and followed through to within a metre or so of the senior Waugh brother to give him the old 'stare'. Tugga naturally replied with, 'What the f*#k are you looking at?', which prompted Curtly to move even closer and snap, 'Don't cuss me, man!' to which Tugga quipped, 'Go and f*#k yourself.' With a full-on fist fight set to erupt, myself and Windies captain Ritchie Richardson both ran in, Richardson dragging his fiery fast-bowler away by the arm, me pushing Steve forward and yelling, 'Have a go at him Tugga!' Three years later the whole ugly incident seems to have been forgotten but we'll find out for sure tomorrow.

There was a great deal of excitement in the village this afternoon as we all prepared for the Opening Ceremony to be held this evening at the main stadium at Bukit Jalil. Everyone got into their official gear

I somehow found myself entering with the women's swimming team. Not that I think anyone noticed.

and headed off in buses. We Aussies were led in by our flag-bearer Kieren Perkins who, given his recent form, may find this the only event he gets to lead in Kuala Lumpur. The plan was for everyone to follow Kieren, grouped in their respective teams but things got a little chaotic and I somehow found myself entering with the women's swimming team. Not that I think anyone noticed.

About 100,000 spectators packed the stadium to witness the Opening Ceremony but, to be perfectly frank, it was a bit of a bore. First we had to sit through the entire history of Malaysia as depicted in dance form. And judging from the length of the performance, Malaysia must have a very long history. After this and about six hours of marching bands stomping around the arena a massive cheer went up, signalling one of two things. Either the Prime Minister had been assassinated or the King had just arrived. It turned out to be the latter, with His Majesty Yang DiPertuan Agong Tuanku Ja'afar ibni Almarhum Tuanku Abdul Rahman (or Yang DiPertuan Agong Tuanku Ja'afar ibni Almarhum Tuanku Abdul for short) officially opening the Games by banging a gong. This momentous occasion was followed by a sixteen-gun salute, which had the locals all ducking for cover. Despite the tedious nature of the event it was great being part of the Australian squad. I must admit when they played our national anthem I felt a lump in my throat which I initially put down to patriotic pride. I later discovered Ponts had dropped a cigarette butt in my beer can, thinking it was empty.

Day 6 ✌ (Sat 12 Sept)

Our second match of the tournament today, a danger game against Antigua. With guys like Richardson, Ambrose and the Benjamin brothers playing for them, not to mention a coach like Viv Richards, this was one team we were taking very seriously. Fortunately Tugga won the toss and sent the Antiguans into bat on the TNB ground. Flem delivered a magnificent opening spell with 5/54, including the prized scalp of Richardson for just 1. With the ball turning sharply and the batsmen prodding it away it was obvious we needed a man at short leg. This position can be very dangerous in these conditions and the risk of serious injury to a player is quite high. I was honoured when Tugga asked me to field there. Wickets continued to fall as the Antigua boys struggled to reach a paltry 99 in the 30th over.

After lunch (well it was more like morning tea) we commenced our innings and, sure enough, copped a fiery opening spell from one Curtly Ambrose. Junior (8) and Bev (2) both fell cheaply, while Ponts was lucky to get a life early on. When I walked out to bat at 3 for 46, things were looking serious. Ambrose was pretty pumped up and I naturally received a fiery welcome. In these situations it's easy to be intimidated — you don't want to do anything that might provoke the bowler. But rather than adopt this gutless attitude I decided to take the fight up to the big West Indian hothead. Next delivery I stepped down the pitch and lobbed the ball back over his head, capping off the moment with a subtle yet offensive gesture. Such a provocative shot was bound to produce a fearsome response from Ambrose, but to tell the truth I wasn't worried. I've been around long enough to handle a bit of intimadatory bowling, and besides, we managed to run a single and Gilly was left on strike. Sure enough, the next ball was an absolute scorcher aimed right at the throat. I was glad to be watching from the non-striker's end. After Gilly retired hurt I went on to make 47 good runs and, along with Tugga, helped to knock off the target in just 18 overs. As for the long-awaited Waugh–Ambrose clash, our skipper reported it was all a thing of the past. Relations were quite civil and according to Tugga at one point Curtly even spoke to him, something along the lines of 'Take this, a*#ehole!'

After an early meal back at the Games Village it was agreed we'd all head off to watch Australia compete in the swimming events. Tugga's very keen on supporting our fellow competitors over here and even though I'm not exactly a big swimming fan there wasn't really much else to do. We tried getting a bus trip organised into a few night-clubs downtown but it simply wasn't possible. This is one aspect of the Games that has been a real eye-opener for me, how poorly some sports are administered. Did you realise that neither the athletics, nor the swimming or cycling teams have their own social committee?

Anyway, we headed off to the pool and it turned out to be a top night, with Australia taking out medal after medal. You almost got sick of hearing our national anthem but it did provide a handy opportunity for us cricketers to start learning the words, something we'll need to do if we're going to be climbing the victory

Curtly even spoke to Steve, something along the lines of 'Take this, a*#ehole!'.

dais in a week or so from now. In addition to receiving medals every winning athlete got a bunch of flowers (even the blokes!) and a small stuffed orang-outang called a *wirra*, which is apparently the Games mascot. As I quipped to one bloke sitting next to me in the stands, it looked more like a miniature version of the Malaysian king!

Day 7 ✌ (Sun 13 Sept)

How was I to know the bloke was a journalist? Of course, the bloody papers over here beat the whole thing up, claiming 'enormous cultural insensitivity', whatever that means. Naturally I was required by team management to release

an apology, draft copies of which I now carry on all tours. It's a handy little document that can basically be tailored to meet any situation.

With no match or training scheduled for today we were free to wander around the village, soaking in the atmosphere of the place. It's obvious we cricketers are something of 'celebrities' among the other athletes here and everywhere I went there were requests for autographs and photos. I'm proud to say that in all my years as an international cricketer I don't think I've ever refused an autograph request, no matter how tired or busy I was (although I will confess to walking upstairs occasionally to shake a kid in a wheelchair — they tend to get real pushy).

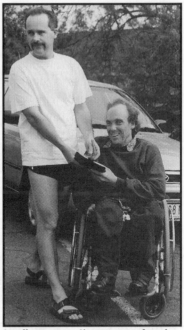

In all my years I've never refused an autograph or photo request.

Day 8 ✌ (Mon 14 Sept)

If there's one thing we cricketers hate on tour it's being woken at some hideously early hour on a rest day and, sure enough, at 11.30 this morning the phone rang. It was our Chef de Mission Don Stockins informing me there had been an official complaint about my behaviour last night at the aquatic centre, in particular the fact I waved a scarf around in the air to help cheer home our relay team. According to Stockins the scarf belonged to a Muslim woman sitting in front of me and, in pulling it off her head, I breached some obscure rule of religious etiquette. All I can say is these Malaysians are a pretty uptight bunch — no wonder they're yet to win a medal.

With my sleep-in ruined I decided to join the boys for lunch, only to be greeted with more bad news. I look like being named 12th man for tomorrow's match. Tugga wants to shuffle the order a little, bump Moods and Boof up, see if we can't get away to a quicker start. Naturally I wasn't happy with the decision but losing your place in a team is all just part of the game and, as Tugga said, the final line-up won't be announced until tomorrow. If anyone is injured or pulls up sore between now and then, I'm back in the team.

This afternoon we had a light training session at the PKNS ground that went pretty well, except for one unfortunate incident. In one of those freak accidents that seem to bedevil some players, promising South Australian batsman Darren 'Boof' Lehmann stepped on an upturned metal rake, lacerating his foot and badly twisting his ankle. I guess it would be easy to blame the ground staff for foolishly leaving such a hazardous piece of equipment lying round on the field, but the fact was the rake had been left outside Boof's room. He trod on it as he stepped out the door. Tugga was furious and immediately started calling for an official inquiry but as I said to him, 'These things happen. Let it go, mate.'

At the team meeting tonight we discussed tomorrow's match, in particular how we'd deal with Indian dangerman Sachin Tendulkar. I tell you, there was a real sense of deja vu about the meeting. We could easily have been back in India — except for the fact none of us had dysentery. Speaking of which, there's been a dengue fever scare in the village with two Australian officials suspected of having contracted the deadly disease. According to our team medicos, it's borne by mosquitoes that breed in damp, humid areas, which basically takes in most of our rooms here at the village.

Day 9 ✌ (Tues 15 Sept)

We woke this morning to another scorcher, the sun beating down as the mercury climbed into the low thirties. But the conditions didn't deter a large crowd of about 5000 assembling at the PKNS ground. This was our first decent crowd of the tournament, predominantly made up of ex-pat Indians waving flags and blowing whistles. Arriving at the ground I was reminded of what I love about Indian cricket fans. Nothing.

For the first time in quite a few games Tugga lost the toss and we were sent in to bat. Whether it was the heat, the heavy clay pitch or just lack of concentration we struggled early, losing quick wickets and really getting tied down by the Indian spinners. I came in with the score at 4 for 78 and tried to push things along, but fell victim to a pretty controversial decision. I was on 17 when I got an edge to a ball from Kumble that flew to gully where Laxman took what he claimed was a great catch. The fact was I'm pretty certain I saw the ball hit the ground before he caught it. Now I would never call Laxman a cheat. I mean, he is, but I'd never call him one. He's got a shocking temper. Anyway, I stood my ground as the two umpires consulted each other as well as the fielder involved. In these tense situations it's very tempting to go over and become embroiled in discussions but experience and maturity has taught me to keep well away. Besides, you can always yell out what you're thinking, which naturally I did. Eventually, however, the decision was made (Todd caught Laxman bowled Kumble for 17, and a $2000 match fine for racial vilification) and the match continued with Tugga (100*) and Moods (76*) combining to knock up a pretty impressive score of 255. Tugga's century was particularly impressive when you consider the appalling temperatures we were playing in. It was so bad that at one point an Indian fielder, Amay Khuresie, actually

Didn't hit the ground my arse...

collapsed from heat exhaustion. He just sort of keeled over and was immediately surrounded by concerned team-mates, as well as Laxman who claimed to have caught him before he hit the ground.

After a short lunch it was time for the Indians to commence their innings and a quick early wicket saw the great man Tendulkar walk to the crease. Fortunately he made just 11 runs before a beautiful ball from Flem sent the batting legend back to the pavilion. At this point a lot of the crowd seemed to lose interest, as did the Indian batsmen, who were quickly dimissed for just 110 runs. Gold medal here we come!

In the other match today New Zealand defeated Pakistan, the Kiwis making 216 and the Pakis probably about $10000 each. So the scene is now set for an Australia vs New Zealand semi-final.

Day 10 ✌ (Wed 16 Sept)

I tell you, the heat over here just seems to get worse. With no air-conditioning in any of the rooms we are forced to sit around in oppressive, humid conditions, watching the temperature soar into the mid-thirties by lunchtime most days. Fortunately we had some relief from this tropical onslaught this afternoon with a massive downpour, caused by one of the guys lighting up under a fire-sprinkler and drenching the entire East Wing.

Needless to say, few of us had much energy left for training so we decided to head off and watch some of the indoor events. One sport

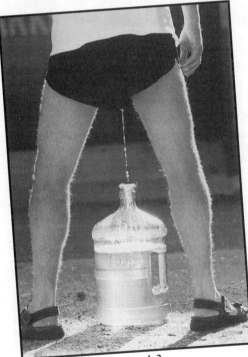

that's absolutely huge over here is tenpin bowling, and Australia's Cara Honeychurch took out yet another gold medal today. Only problem for her came after the win when she was led off by officials for probably the first drug test of her career. Almost one hour and several litres of water later the test tube was apparently still dry! I'm proud to say this is a problem that has never affected me as the old Todd kidneys work pretty well — it's only my liver that needs a bit of maintenance.

You wanted a urine sample?

Day 11 ✌ (Thur 17 Sept)

The first semi-final between South Africa and Sri Lanka was played yesterday with the jungle-bunnies defeating the tea-baggers easily. Today it was our turn to stake a claim for a finals berth — all we had to do was defeat New Zealand. Down at the Kilat Club Tugga yet again won the toss and we sent the Kiwis in, expecting a decent fight. Instead they completely caved in, crashing to 6 for 58 at one point after inspired performances from Flem and Kaspa. At this point Youngie stepped in and delivered the killer blow with an amazing hat-trick that had some commentators referring to the young South Australian as 'find of the series'. It's funny, isn't it? How a flashy, one-off spin-bowling effort so often overshadows solid, consistent, determined batting performances. Still, good luck to Youngie, it was a great effort. Obviously the substandard pitch and the inexperienced New Zealand batting line-up had a lot to do with things, as did the humid conditions, but none of those factors should be allowed to take away from a great individual performance. However, let's just list those factors again:

1) Substandard pitch.

2) Inexperienced batting line-up.

3) Humid conditions so conducive to swing even I could have taken a wicket. (In fact, I almost did. With the Kiwis obviously down and out Tugga tossed me the ball in the 26th over and I delivered a pretty impressive spell of left-arm orthodox (1–0–6–0 4nb 2w). I don't often get the chance to bowl these days but in the past experts have compared me with Sri Lanka's Muttiah Muralidaran. Not only do we have similar actions, we both get reported to the match referee on a fairly regular basis.)

159

Controversial Sri Lankan Muttiah Muralidaran.   Controversial Australian Warwick Todd.

Despite the very low score posted by New Zealand we have learnt never to take any win for granted and, sure enough, Junior fell just a few overs in for only 10, sparking a frantic dash for our Number Three, Ponts, who had to find his pads and get a bus back from the Games Village where he'd headed off to organise the semi-final victory party. Fortunately he made it just in time and together with Gilly managed to compile the required runs.

Naturally there was a lot of media excitement surrounding Youngie's hat-trick with everyone wanting interviews and photos. And back at the village there was a huge pile of 'hero-grams' waiting for him. As an experienced member of the team I know how dangerous this new-found fame can be, so I took the liberty of hiding the faxes — for his own good, of course. The combination of success and spin bowling can be a lethal one, as we've all learnt over recent years. Let it get out of hand and next thing you know the guy will be wearing an earring and doing Nike ads.

After a few quiet drinks at the village, Tugga once again led a contingent off to the aquatic centre. Our skipper really loves his swimming, either that or he just likes watching young girls in Speedos. Tonight was a special one, featuring the final of the men's 1500 metres freestyle. Unfortunately the star of the event Kieren Perkins managed only third place. There's no doubt he's a champion athlete but if you ask me, Perkins has spent too much time over recent years pursuing his extensive corporate and commercial responsibilities and not enough time putting in the hard yards at training.

Day 12 ✌ (Fri 18 Sep)

Our final training session this morning but I was unable to attend due to some problems with a TV commercial I shot before leaving Australia. I spent about two hours on the phone with my manager Gabe Hirsh, who informed me that the client, some Queensland-based agricultural pump manufacturer, now wants to super the words 'Warwick Todd — Cricketer' over the opening shot of me when I emerge from behind the tank stand. According to Gabe, the client is worried — get this — that 'people may not recognise me'! Twelve years as an international cricketer, my own cable-TV nature series, twice used as a celebrity face on the *Sale of the Century* Fame Game board, a regular traffic segment on Adelaide breakfast radio ('Toddy's Traffic Update') and people won't recognise me? Give me a break. In the end I simply told Gabe to sort it out as I had more important things to do down at the ground. It was close to midday and if I didn't get a move-on I'd miss lunch.

The afternoon was spent relaxing at the village, mentally preparing for the big final tomorrow. The last week or so has gone by in a bit of a blur really but we've enjoyed every minute of it — if you exclude some of the dance routines from the Opening Ceremony. And the spirit of the Games has been great too, certainly among us cricketers. We've been able to meet and mingle with inferior teams from all over the world and then go out and mercilessly crush them on the field. Sadly, the Games spirit was slightly soured today by Aussie cyclist Lucy Tyler-Sharman who effectively accused her team of sabotage after she failed to win a race. After a hastily convened meeting, Games officials have apparently called for her immediate expulsion from the Australian contingent. Good thing too.

At the team meeting tonight Tugga spoke about the need to stay focused and not start 'counting our chickens' too early. South Africa

Cyclist Lucy Tyler-Sharman attempts to dodge press cameras after expulsion from the Games Village.

Cricketer Warwick Todd attempts to dodge press cameras after returning to the Games Village at 5.30 am on the morning of the final.

are a formidable team and playing well and Tugga was keen to go through each player, identifying his strengths and weaknesses. As is now common practice with Australian team meetings, videos came in very handy, not only to replay past games but also to tape the meeting for those of us who were out having a few drinks with the women's hockey team and missed the meeting.

Day 13 ✌ (Sat 19 Sept)

Well, I won't dwell on the details. Most of them are a bit of a blur anyway. But we blew it. We came *that* close to a gold medal and then let it slip through our fingers.

The day began poorly with Tugga losing the toss and South African captain Shaun Pollock deciding to send us in. Junior, Ponts and Gilly all fell cheaply to have us reeling at 3 for 28. For a while it looked like Tugga and Boof (recently recovered from his garden rake mishap) might steady the ship, but then Boof fell for 26. I joined Tugga out in the middle and we slowly managed to push the score up to 183 in the second last over. Tugga had been playing beautifully and, with just six balls to go was on 89 — not that I think he knew it. Tugga's one of those players who doesn't like to keep close track of his score, especially when approaching a ton, in case it causes him to become nervous and lose concentration. So during our mid-wicket conference before the final over I naturally quipped, 'Only eleven runs to go, mate. Good luck with the century.' After that he sort of fell apart, playing and missing at several balls before scrambling through for a suicidal single that saw me well short at the other end.

During the lunchbreak the mood was quite upbeat with most of the guys convinced a score of 183 could still be competitive. Now I'm as optimistic as the next bloke but for some reason I had my doubts. Just a niggling suspicion that we weren't fully 'on song'. Sure, I know anyone reading this will be thinking, 'That's easy to say in hindsight, Toddy', but I can produce the betting coupon I took out on a South African victory stamped 1.47 pm Malaysian time. As it turned out, my gut instincts were right and we played badly this afternoon. For the first time our fielding let us down. There's no point in naming names, Junior and Flem both know they made costly mistakes. Thanks to this

A disappointing end to the Games.

and some decent batting from the South Africans, our total of 183 was easily passed in the 47th over — leaving Australia a disappointing second and collecting nothing but a silver medal, a bunch of flowers and a crappy stuffed ape.

After the official medal ceremony was over we quickly regrouped and decided to head downtown to drown our sorrows with a few cleansing ales. However, back at the Games Village word was out that there had been some political unrest in the capital and all athletes were being advised to stay well away. But we figured there couldn't be too much harm in visiting a few pubs so we grabbed a fleet of taxis and headed off for a quiet night on the town.

Day 14 ✌ (Sun 20 Sept)

Games City Explodes as Mahathir Strikes Back — Aussie Cricketer Urges on Mob

● By Yassof Mutjaba

Australian cricketer Warwick Todd at the centre of violent protest.

AAP — Sat 19 Malaysia was last night in crisis after thousands of demonstrators stormed the streets demanding the resignation of Prime Minister Dr Mahathir Mohamad. The violent protests followed the arrest of sacked Deputy Prime Minister Mr Anwar Ibrahim. Early last night riot police repeatedly fired water cannons and tear gas at 800 demonstrators who converged on the city centre. The crowd intermittently shouted 'Long Live Anwar', 'Allahu Akbar' (God is Greatest) and 'Aussie Aussie Aussie, Oy, Oy, Oy', the latter chant coming from Australian cricketer Warwick Todd who had somehow become caught up in the mob unrest. Eyewitnesses reported seeing the controversial batsman urging the crowd on with a stream of both anti-government and anti-South African obscenities before grabbing a fire hose and (continued page 2)

I woke with quite a headache at some ungodly hour this morning, improved in no way by the sound of the phone ringing. It turned out to be my manager Gabe, who wanted to know if I'd seen a copy of the newspaper that morning. I hadn't, but one look at the front page reminded me of why I had such a bad headache. Gabe sounded pretty worked up, suggesting I get out of the country as soon as possible. 'Don't over-react,' I told him. 'It's only a small article on the front page.' That's when he dropped the bombshell. 'Toddy, I'm talking about what's on the sports page.'

Todd in Tampering Scandal!!!

Australian cricketer Warwick Todd caught off guard during yesterday's final against South Africa.

Time to head home.

Index

Photographic Credits